Reviews for Kevin Norley's books

'I found *Making Britain Literate* an excellent, comprehensive and thought-provoking book. Crucially, it should be an extremely effective tool and a remedy for all kinds of entrenched malaise within our educational system. And it manages to combine rigour with accessibility and fun. It deserves great praise.'

Lee M, The Plain English Campaign

'*Making Britain Literate* and *Making Britain Numerate*… cover key requirements for teaching basic literacy and numeracy. Suitable for professional teachers and homeschoolers, both books include helpful examples and exercises.'

Newsletter No 70, Spring 2010, Campaign for Real Education

'I recently passed both my L2 literacy and numeracy at Bedford College. I found the ideas contained in both Mr Norley's books really useful. I developed a better understanding of English (which is my second language), particularly with the grammar, which even helped me with my maths.'

Marilyn L (Bedford College, June 2010)

'(*Making Britain Numerate*) is a superb book which can be used as a study guide for anyone wishing to improve their own numeracy skills, or help someone else with theirs. I have used it with many of my staff and all have commented at how easy it is to grasp the concepts within it. All have shown improvements in their numeracy skills.'

Steve W, Area Manager, VT Training, East of England, March 2009, Amazon.co.uk

'I have recently finished a maths course at the Luton Learning Centre. There were 15 of us on the course, from all different parts of the world. Kevin showed us very clearly how to work with fractions and percentages, how to convert from one to the other, and how those conversions can be used to both better understand and solve problems including those involving scale and volume. His explanations were detailed, and he had high expectations of all of us. Needless to say, I achieved my L2 numeracy qualification.'

Caroline O (Luton Learning Centre, July '10)

'I needed a level 2 numeracy qualification in order to be accepted onto a BSc Social Work and Mental Health Nursing degree course, so I attended a numeracy workshop at the Skillsbank. The resources used and methods taught from '*Making Britain Numerate*' were very straightforward and ideal for ensuring that I obtained my qualification quickly!'

Charity M (Bedford College, June '10)

'The level 3 numeracy staff training carried out by Mr Norley was based on a range of strategies that built on clear and precise methods, all of which are detailed in his book, *Making Britain Numerate*. All the group passed their level 3 application of number test."

Kevin G, Internal Verifier - Training, Babcock International Group

'One of the things I find interesting about *Making Britain Literate*, is that it attempts to address both the literacy and language needs of native speakers and ESOL students in one book. It values, for example, the importance of the understanding of grammar and word classes in developing literacy and language skills.'

Michael M, English Language Tutor, Challney Community College, Luton

For further reviews, go to
www.skillsforlifenetwork.com/making-britain-numerate-literate

Making Britain Numerate

Kevin Norley

Imprimata

Published by **Imprimata**
Copyright © Kevin Norley 2008, 2011

2nd Edition 2011

A CIP Catalogue record for this book is available
from the British Library

ISBN 978-1-906192-49-5

Printed in Great Britain

Imprimata

An imprint of InXmedia Limited
www.imprimata.co.uk

In loving memory of my father

Rationale

I really like my job, working as an essential skills trainer for a training organisation, traversing the countryside and urban conurbations of the Eastern counties of England, supporting learners in the workplace with their numeracy and literacy skills. The learners I work with have been signed up by my organisation onto a range of apprenticeship, advanced apprenticeship and Train to Gain programmes within the hospitality, sport, care and retail sectors. During the learner's sign up, they take an initial assessment in numeracy and literacy. If, following their initial assessment, they score below a certain level, they are referred to me for support with their numeracy or literacy (or both) in order to achieve their L1 or L2 key skills (application of number and communication) qualification as part of their apprenticeship programme or adult numeracy or literacy (L1 or L2) qualification as part of their 'Skills for life' (Train to Gain) programme. This usually means achieving Entry Level 3, regarded as equivalent to a level an average 9 year old should be working at. Learners are also referred to me it they achieve L1 (regarded as equivalent to a level an average 11 year old should be working at) but choose to receive support or are required to achieve L2 adult numeracy or reach L2 in their key skills.

The workplaces include pubs, hotels, sports centres, care homes, canteens within army barracks, cafes, shops, restaurants etc. The learners themselves are any age (16+) but most fall with the 16 to 24 age range. They come from across the country, although most are from the East of England.

However, I really needn't be doing my job. What I mean is, 'Why, after 11 years of schooling, do learners require support in the basics of numeracy and/or literacy?'

The job requires plenty of driving around and with it lots of listening to the radio. Ironically, not much time goes by without one report or another criticising the state of basic skills of our workforce, be it school leavers, or even graduates, entering the job market. For example, the Leitch review (2006: 1) entitled 'Prosperity for all in the global economy', a report commissioned by the government to consider the UK's long term skills needs, concluded that 'almost one half of adults (17 million) have difficulties with numbers' and that 'continuing to improve our schools will not be enough' on the basis that 'over 70% of our 2020 workforce have already completed their compulsory education'.

Furthermore, a recent CBI survey (2006), entitled 'Working on the Three Rs' which took the views of 735 firms employing 1.7 million staff and was funded by the DfES, reiterates the mantra of school leavers lacking the required numeracy and literacy skills for the world of work. It states that, 'Poor basic skills damage people's lives and their employment prospects' and that, 'Weak functional skills are associated with higher unemployment, lower earnings, poorer chances of career progression and social exclusion.'

The extent and effects of poor numeracy amongst adults in society were also highlighted in the Moser report (1999), which claimed that more than one in five adults in Britain are not functionally numerate. The importance of numeracy in relation to employment was outlined in the report (1999: 25) which stated that, 'almost every job now requires some competence in basic skills', whilst in relation to earnings (1999: 23), '... low earnings are much more likely if one has poor basic skills than if one has good basic skills.' Reflecting on the causes of poor numeracy within the population at large, the report (1999: 10) stated that, 'The situation has come about from home circumstances and above all, from poor schooling'. Each of the above reports also talks about the cost to the British economy as a whole, as well as to the individual.

More recently, an OFSTED report carried out by its Chief Inspector (Christine Gilbert) warned that in some schools, its pupils were being held back by its teachers' poor grasp of maths and science (OFSTED, Nov 2009). Around about the same time, it was being reported that business leaders were complaining that youngsters were leaving school without the basic skills they need in the workplace (www.dailytelegraph.com, Nov 24th 2009). Sir Stuart Rose (Chairman of Marks and Spencer), for example, was reported as saying that, 'They cannot do reading. They cannot do arithmetic. They cannot do writing.'

Along with reports detailing issues relating to the extent and effects of poor basic skills on individuals, employers and society in general, there has not been a lack of initiatives over the years attempting to address the issues, including, for example, the introduction of Standard Attainment Tests (SATS) in schools, league tables, OFSTED, the National Curriculum and the national numeracy and literacy strategy.

In terms of post-16 education, the adult numeracy and literacy core curricula along with L1 and L2 national tests in numeracy and literacy were introduced as part of the government's 'Skills for Life strategy', launched in 2001, the aim of which was 'to improve the literacy, language and numeracy skills of 1.5m adults in England' by 2007, including young people and adults in low-skilled jobs. However, in spite of apparently billions of pounds of investment in the scheme, it was reported by Smithers (2006: 1) in 'The Guardian' that according to a new report, 'Up to 16 million adults – nearly half the workforce – are holding down jobs despite having the reading and writing skills expected of children leaving primary school ...' and that the scheme had 'done little to improve the quality of literacy and numeracy teaching'.

Furthermore, it was reported by Curtis (2008: 4) in 'The Guardian' that the schools minister Lord Adonis had told them that, '... the 20% of pupils who leave primary school lacking basic skills in reading, writing and mathematics is the biggest failure of the Labour government's education policies.' In the same article, on reflecting on the GCSE results in 2008, it was reported that, '... around half of 16 year-olds will fail to achieve the government's target of five good GCSEs including English and maths'. Of course, similar statistics can be seen year in, year out, along with questions on the lines of, 'Will there ever be any change to the status quo to any significant degree?'

Although understanding of issues relating to numeracy difficulties that learners face in society can on the one hand come from reports such as those already mentioned, they also need to come from one's own direct experience of working with learners.

So why are so many school leavers still leaving school without the basics? Why too, in spite of much investment, do so many adults still lack the basics? And what actually works?

Indeed, much has been written about the reasons behind poor numeracy, and the problems it causes to both the individual and society in general. However, what I believe to be lacking is solutions in the form of ideas, methods and resources that can be used successfully with learners to improve their numeracy skills.

What this book attempts to do is to show those methods, describe the context in which they are used and provide contextualised resources in which they can be demonstrated. Of course supporting learners with numeracy is not just about resources and methods, it's about how it's put across, the enthusiasm of the tutor, and their ability to motivate learners and make it relevant to their needs.

In terms of audience, the resources are intended primarily for learners who are studying functional skills mathematics as part of an apprenticeship or advanced apprenticeship programme and/or a Skills for Life qualification (L1 or L2 adult numeracy) in a further education or work-based learning setting. However, beyond that, I believe that they are suitable for any adult who struggles with numeracy and who wishes to improve their everyday numeracy skills. The L1 numeracy learning assessment and practice questions together with the L2 numeracy learning guide can be used directly by learners or can be used to assist tutors in supporting their learners.

I believe that the L1 numeracy learning assessment sets a minimum standard for any learner studying for a programme that requires any degree of numerical skills (including L1 functional skills mathematics and L1 adult numeracy) and sets a minimum standard for any person dealing with everyday numeracy.

It was mentioned earlier with reference to a variety of reports and reviews, that many employers find their employees lacking the basics. In light of these concerns, the L1 learning assessment, or L2 learning guide, could be used as a recruitment tool by employers who may wish their prospective employees to be able to demonstrate competence in numeracy to a given level, depending on the nature of the job. This may seem harsh, but I believe that in raising the bar, it could potentially have a knock on effect back to schools to ensure that those who leave have a command of the basics, preferably long before they leave, and on individuals themselves seeking employment who would hopefully be able to appreciate more the importance of everyday numeracy, both for themselves and their prospective employer.

When helping a learner with their numeracy, then of course it's good to be patient; patience is a virtue after all. However, at the same time, unless you have the patience of a saint, an element of frustration and impatience will almost certainly come into play. With work-based learners for example, there's the constant issue of time; they're on a break and need to start work soon; they just need to go, for a whole host of reasons. As a tutor too, there's paperwork, phone calls to return, emails to write and respond to, and other appointments to move onto etc so the impatience comes from not having the time to cover what you wish. In terms of frustration, this can come from witnessing the learner's lack of ability to carry out, or understand, mathematical operations such as division, multiplication, subtraction, forming and simplifying a fraction, and calculating percentages, and sometimes from their lack of commitment or understanding of the potential usefulness of developing and using such skills. As stated in the afore-mentioned report, 'Working on the three Rs' for example:

> '**Percentages are widely used in internal communications and in many jobs it is essential to be able to calculate them readily. A functionally numerate person should therefore be able to calculate a percentage and interpret the significance of percentages communicated to them.'**
> *(CBI 2006: 3)*

The report (2006: 3) also states that, 'As well as percentages, a mathematically literate person will be able to work comfortably with fractions, decimals and ratios' and that, 'Multiplication tables and mental arithmetic without using a calculator constitute an essential aid in all sorts of work activities'.

A part of the difficulty that learners often face is the ability to set out a sum in a suitable format for it to be solved, as well as being able to do the required calculation once they have set it out in a suitable format.

As well as the concepts, learners often lack the required knowledge to carry out calculations, such as knowing that to calculate an area you need to multiply the length by the width, that there are a thousand grams in a kilogram, a thousand metres in a kilometre and a hundred centimetres in a metre, and that the range of a group of numbers is the difference between the highest and the lowest number within that group and so on.

With all this in mind, I should get to the point:

After introductions, I outline to the learner that there are two points I wish to emphasise; firstly, the fact that the numeracy I cover is relevant both to their job role and their everyday life, and secondly that none of the work that they cover will be difficult. I then explain that it is my job to persuade, or try and convince, them of the above two points.

'I saw a pair of shoes in a sale on my way here. Their normal price was £30.00 but there was a 20% discount. Do you know how to calculate 20% of £30.00 (and how much they'd cost with the discount)?

If so, then fine. They can outline how they do it, and we can move onto further, perhaps more difficult examples.

If however they can't do it, then I say OK, leave that to one side a minute. Then, on a separate piece of paper I ask:

'What's three times ten (3.0 x 10)?' to which the learner would normally reply

'**30**', then

'What's six multiplied by ten (6.0 x 10)?' to which the learner would normally reply

'**60**'

and '7.0 x 10?' '**70**'.

Next, 'What's six and a half times ten
(6.5 x 10)?'

They may say '**65**' If they don't, I show them the pattern of the decimal point moving one point to the right, which increases the size of the number tenfold. Once they've picked up on that, I ask the learner to write down £12.50 x 10 and guide them, if necessary, through reinforcing the above pattern, to the answer:

£12.50 x 10 = £**125.00**

This can be followed up by further examples until the learner 'gets the hang of it'.

A good follow up example to try is £12.05 x 10

The learner may say (or write) £125.00 in which case the difference with the above can be pointed out, say (or write) £120.05 in which case the difference in sequence of numbers needs to be pointed out, or say (or write) £120.5 in which case it needs to be pointed out that when writing money, there should be 2 numbers after the decimal point, so the answer would be £**120.50**

Ask the learner to pick the price of something out of the air, for example:

'£6.42'

'OK, so how much would ten of those cost?' and guide the learner towards:

£6.42 x 10 = £**64.20**

Some learners may continue to have difficulty with this method in seeing the sequence of numbers (e.g. in the above example they may say sixty four pounds and two pence or write £64.02 or £64.2 instead of £64.20) so they may need to have the method reinforced with further examples.

(It's one thing writing all this down, but naturally it has to be done with some enthusiasm, the voice can be slightly raised and positive encouragement given.)

Following on from this, I would ask the learner:

'OK, so if £12.50 x 10 is £125.00 then what's £12.50 divided by 10?'

If they're able to state the correct answer, then I would ask them to show how they came to the answer, and build on that with further examples. If they're not sure, I would say something like:

'When we multiplied by 10 earlier, we moved the decimal point one place to the right, making the number ten times bigger, so when we divide by 10 we …'

Here the answer can be elicited along the lines of 'we make the number ten times smaller by moving the decimal point one point to the left', (substantially reducing the size of the number):

So, £12.50 ÷ 10 = £1.25 (and 10% of £64.00 = £6.40 and so on)

This can be followed by further examples, again checking that the learner is able to maintain the correct sequence of numbers, for example:

£160.50 ÷ 10 = £16.05 and so on until the learner 'gets the hang of it'.

I would then ask the learner 'ok, so now what's 10% of £12.50?'

If the connection is made that calculating 10% of a number is the same as dividing by 10 and the answer comes back as £1.25 then fine. Either way, I would ask the question,

'What does per cent mean? or what does 10% mean? Or 25%'

If the learner is unsure, or unable to give a clear answer, I would say something like, 'It means, 'Out of a hundred'. Ten per cent means ten out of a hundred, and twenty five per cent means twenty five out of a hundred and so on. Cent means a hundred. For example there are a hundred centimetres in a metre and a hundred cents in a dollar. Cent means a hundred in French. So, ten percent means 10 out of a hundred, which can be written as a fraction':

$$\frac{10}{100}$$

This can be simplified to...

$$\frac{1}{10}$$

by cancelling a nought from the top with a nought from the bottom:

$$\frac{1\cancel{0}}{10\cancel{0}} = \frac{1}{10}$$

(or by saying that 10 will go into a 100 ten times and into itself once.)

So, 10% is the same as a tenth (1/10).

To calculate...

$$\frac{1}{10}$$

(or 10%) of a number then, we need to divide that number by 10.

Going back to our example above then, I would ask the learner to calculate the following (guiding them through if necessary):

10% of £1$\overset{\frown}{2}$.50 = **£1.25**

Similarly, going back to the example with the discount on the shoes:

10% of £3$\overset{\frown}{0}$.00 = **£3.00**

So, if 10% of £30.00 = £3.00 then what would 20% be?

20% is double 10% so 20% = £3.00 x 2 = **£6.00**

So, with the discount, the cost of the shoes would be
£30.00 – £6.00 = **£24.00**

Or
$$
\begin{array}{r}
£\ ^2 3\,^1 0.00 \\
-\ £\ \ \ \ 6.00 \\
\hline
£\ \ \mathbf{24.00}
\end{array}
$$

The learner can then be asked to work through a similar example, following the same method:

> **30% off trainers!**
>
> **Retail Price: £45.00**
>
> **Sale Price: £** ....

10% of £45.00 = £4.50   30% of £45.00 = £4.50
$$
\begin{array}{r}
\text{x}\ \ \ \ \ 3 \\
\hline
£\ \mathbf{13.50} \\
\hline
\scriptstyle 1
\end{array}
$$

So, sale price =
$$
\begin{array}{r}
£\ \ 4^4 5^1.00 \\
-\ £\ \ 13.50 \\
\hline
£\ \ \mathbf{31.50}
\end{array}
$$

If necessary, this can be followed up by further examples to reinforce the methods.

Obviously it helps a lot if the learner knows their times tables. Generally, if for whatever reason an adult learner does not know their times tables by the time they've left school, then they will continue to struggle. An adult learner can still improve however through a combination of trying to recite their tables, consistent referencing to the tables in order to become more familiar with the numbers which appear, practice in writing them out and using them in calculations, along with any other method a learner may find appropriate (such as using their fingers). If the learner continues to struggle, then they can be prompted to write the relevant part of the times tables they are using in a column, by adding the relevant number consecutively, for example:

	8			6	
(+10−2)	16		(+6)	12	
(+10−2)	24		(+6)	18	
(+10−2)	32	etc	(+6)	24	etc

Next, I may say something like, 'A cup of coffee costs £1.85 how much would it cost to buy 20 cups of coffee?

Again, the learner is given the opportunity to work it out using any method they choose. If they're able to calculate it correctly then that's fine. If not, I would ask the learner, 'OK, so how much would 10 cups of coffee cost?' then if necessary remind them or guide them through the process:

£1.85 x 10 = **£18.50**

Then I would ask, 'OK, so if the cost of 10 cups of coffee is £18.50, then what would be the cost of 20 cups of coffee?', eliciting from the learner the need to double £18.50 by either

$$
\begin{array}{r}
£\ 18.50 \\
+\ £\ 18.50 \\
\hline
£\ \mathbf{37.00} \\
\hline
{\scriptstyle 11}
\end{array}
\qquad\text{or}\qquad
\begin{array}{r}
£\ 18.50 \\
\times\ \ \ 2 \\
\hline
£\ \mathbf{37.00} \\
\hline
{\scriptstyle 11}
\end{array}
$$

Following on from this example, I would take a similar example whereby the same method can be transferred.

'OK, so a chef earns £6.45 per hour, how much would he earn in 30 hours?' If the learner needs to be prompted, then again it's, 'How much would he earn in 10 hours?'

£6.45 x 10 = **£64.50**

This time eliciting from the learner the need to treble the result, on the basis that 30 is treble (or 3 times) 10

$$
\begin{array}{r}
£\ 64.50 \\
\times\ \ \ 3 \\
\hline
£\ \mathbf{193.50} \\
\hline
{\scriptstyle 1\ 1}
\end{array}
$$

Another area of difficulty that many learners face is the concept of fractions and the ability to convert from fractions to percentages (and vice-versa). For this I often begin with the following table:

Fractions/Percentages/Decimal Conversion Table

	Fraction	Percentage	Decimal
	1/2 (a half)	50%	0.5

To begin with then, I make the assumption that they'd be able to follow the first line. In other words, I'd say something like, 'OK, you go into a restaurant which is half full. What's that as a percentage?' Following on from their answer, 'It's half full or 50 per cent full, right. This can be shown as a fraction (1/2), as a percentage (50%) or as a decimal. As a decimal, a half is written as 0.5 Think of a pound (£1.00). A half of a pound is 50p, which is written (in pounds) as £0.50'

'Looking at the next line, what fraction does the pie chart show, or represent?' Most will recognise this as a quarter, and be able to write it as ¼. If not, the learner can be led to the answer by being asked how many parts there are in the chart (4), and of those how many are shaded (1). So, 1 part out of 4 is shaded, which means that the pie chart shows a … a quarter, 1/4. As a percentage then, the learner is likely to know that a quarter correlates with 25%, but if not a quarter can be shown via the pie charts as a half of a half, and that a half of 50% is … 25%. For the decimal equivalent then, the learner may deduce (or be led to) the answer of 0.25 by halving 0.5

Similarly, three quarters (3/4) can be elicited from the learner, along with 75% (illustrating the sequence of 25%, 50% and 75%) and 0.75 (illustrating the pattern of how the decimal relates to the percentage i.e. 50% = 0.5 25% = 0.25 and 75% = 0.75 etc

As well as writing ¼ in the relevant part of the above table, I ask the learner to write it in words. In so doing, they may miss out the 'r' between the 'a' and the 't'. Similarly then, this is done for all the other fractions in the table. Learners may also have difficulties in writing the word 'fifth', omitting the letter 'f' in the middle for example. I explain that in numeracy it's important also to be able to recognise and be able to spell numbers (or fractions) in words.

It's normally on the next line when learners can become stuck or begin to struggle. Initially (again you can illicit from the pie chart,) one part out of five, expressed as a fifth and written as 1/5 can be elicited from the learner with the help of the pie chart. When it comes to converting from the fraction to the percentage, some learners will struggle. In this case I say something like, 'OK, imagine you have 5 friends sitting over there and you have a hundred pounds which you want to share between them. How much would they each get?' At this point they may get it straight away, or say maybe 15 pounds, at which point I would reply something like, 'OK, so if they get £15 each, that would be 15, 30, 45, 60, 75 total, so you'd have £25 left over'. If they don't come up with the answer themselves then I say something along the lines of, 'OK, so we need to divide £100 between 5 people. This can be shown as £100 ÷ 5 and set out as:

$$100 \div 5 = 5\overline{)100}^{\,020}$$

So, five doesn't go into 1, so you can put a 0 above the 1
Then, how many fives are there in 10? 2 which goes above the 0
Then, how many times does five go into 0? 0 which goes above the 0

So, the answer is that they each get £20

i.e. a fifth (1/5) of a hundred is 20 so a fifth is equivalent to 20% which expressed as a decimal is 0.2

Next, 2 parts out of 5 i.e. 2/5 (two fifths) is elicited from the learner. From here they're generally away, but may need a nudge in the form of, 'Well, looking at the pie charts, 2/5 is double or twice as much as 1/5, would you agree? So, 2/5 as a percentage will be twice as much as 20% which is … 40% which expressed as a decimal is … 0.4 or 0.40' and then they're away for 3/5 = 60% = 0.60 and 4/5 = 80% = 0.8

When it comes to the last one in the table, a similar process to the one above can be gone through i.e. one part out of three, expressed as a third and written as 1/3 can be elicited from the learner with the help of the pie chart. If they struggle again to convert from the fraction to the percentage, I would say, 'ok, now you've got three friends sitting over there, and you've got £100 which you want to share between them. How much would they each get?' The reply is often £30 in which case I say, '30, 60, 90 so that doesn't quite work as you'd have £10 left over' or £35 I which case I say, '35, 70, 105 so I'm afraid that doesn't work either'. I then say to the learner, 'OK, you now have 3 friends sitting over there, so you now need to divide £100 by 3 and ask the learner to follow the same procedure as dividing by 5, stating that it does not go in exactly, but that we can give the percentage to the nearest whole number (i.e. 33%). The final table will then end up like so:

Fractions/Percentages/Decimal Conversion Table

		Fraction	Percentage	Decimal
		1/2 (a half)	50%	0.5
		1/4 (a quarter)	25%	0.25
		3/4 (three quarters)	75%	0.75
		1/5 (a fifth)	20%	0.2

	2/5 (two fifths)	40%	0.4
	3/5 (three fifths)	60%	0.6
	4/5 (four fifths)	80%	0.8
	1/3 (a third)	33%	0.33

To illustrate this further, examples should be given whereby the relationship between percentages, fractions and decimals can be reinforced:

eg 1. There are 330 pupils in a primary school. If 40% of them are boys, then calculate the number of boys in the primary school.

10% of 330 = 33

so 40% of 330 = 33
$$\begin{array}{r} \times\ 4 \\ \hline \mathbf{132} \\ \hline {\scriptstyle 1} \end{array}$$

we also know that 40% as a fraction $= \dfrac{40}{100} = \dfrac{4}{10} = \dfrac{2}{5}$

To calculate two fifths of 330:

$$330 \times \dfrac{2}{5} = \dfrac{660}{5} = 5\overline{)6^16^10} \ \dfrac{132}{} = \mathbf{132}$$

40% as a decimal $= \dfrac{40}{100} = 0.4$

To calculate 330 x 0.4

300 x 0.4 = 3 x 100 x 0.4 = 3 x 40 = 120

$30 \times 0.4 = 3 \times 10 \times 0.4 = 3 \times 4 = 12$

$120 + 12 = 132$

Eg 2. There are 180 players in a football competition. If a quarter of them are under 21, then calculate the number of players who are under 21.

$$\frac{1}{4} \times 180 = 4\overline{)1\,8^20} \quad \frac{0\,4\,5}{} = \mathbf{45}$$

A quarter as a percentage $= \dfrac{1}{4} \times 100\% = 25\%$

10% of 180 = 18   20% = 36   5% = 9

So, 25% = 36 + 9 = 45

$$\frac{1}{4} \text{ as a decimal } = 4\overline{)1.0^20} \quad \frac{0.2\,5}{}$$

To calculate 180 x 0.25

$100 \times 0.25 = 25$

$80 \times 0.25 = 8 \times 10 \times 0.25 = 8 \times 2.5 = 2.5$

$$\begin{array}{r} 2.5 \\ \times\ 8 \\ \hline 20.0 \\ \end{array}$$

25 + 20 = 45

In both of the above examples, it's a case of choosing the most appropriate method.

However, the calculations involving the decimals are quite long-winded and complicated relative to the methods involving percentages or fractions. Nevertheless, the methods used in the calculations involving decimals can be useful (for example, see 'Calculations involving Multiplication' p59–62 and p95–97).

If learners are given further examples and questions in order to reinforce their knowledge and understanding of equivalences, then with practice, they should be able to develop a 'numerical instinct' whereby they will be able to convert from one to the other as necessary and choose the most appropriate method for each problem.

Following on from this then, learners can be given everyday examples of calculating a fifth, a quarter and a third in order to consolidate the idea of a fraction as part of a whole and to reinforce the technique of division. For example:

'The bill for a meal for a group of 5 people comes to £88.00 If they decide to split the bill evenly, then how much would they each pay?'

$$£88.00 \div 5 = 5\overline{)\,8^3 8 \cdot{}^3 00} = £\textbf{17.60}$$

with the quotient 1 7.60 written above.

Here, the idea of a fifth being the same as 20% can be reinforced through asking the learner to calculate 20% of £88.00

So, 10% of £88.00 = £8.80

Then 20% = £8.80
        x   2
        £**17.60**
          1

Division, and the context in which it is used, can be further reinforced through examples calculating the average of a group of numbers. Naturally it's important to be able to relate examples to the learner's job role with some enthusiasm on the one hand, whilst being able to anticipate the difficulties they're likely to have and errors they're likely to make on the other.

Before moving on from the conversion table, I ask the learner if they can calculate say, '40 x 0.5' in their head. If they're not able to, I ask them, 'OK, so what's half of forty?' to which they would normally reply '20'. The point here is simply to remind the learner that 0.5 is equivalent to a half.

I mentioned earlier that learners were referred to me following an initial assessment. Initial assessments are either paper-based or carried out on a laptop. Whilst on the one hand the learners that are referred to me have been identified as having difficulties with numeracy, they have invariably not had the opportunity to learn from the initial assessments themselves i.e. there has been no input into the learning process and hence I believe a learning opportunity has been lost. Many of the questions in the initial assessments are not contextualised, and some of the questions are multiple choice (hence allowing for an element of guesswork), whilst others just contain blank spaces to put in the answer. As such, workings out (where relevant) are not shown (e.g. carrying over in addition and multiplication, borrowing/paying back with subtraction and carrying over the remainder with division, and changing the place value when multiplying (or dividing) a number by 10 etc.) and so types of error cannot be identified. As a result, learners can end up with similar scores, yet whilst some may really struggle with reading and/or have quite severe learning difficulties others are just a little rusty and need reminding of relevant and appropriate methods to answer questions. Another issue relating to assessments carried out on a laptop includes the fact that answers for calculations involving addition, subtraction and multiplication have to be input from left to right whereas they are normally input from right to left.

Furthermore, where the initial assessment is followed by a diagnostic assessment, the diagnostic assessment breaks the skills down into areas such as fractions and percentages as opposed to areas such as:

'Calculating Percentages', 'Forming and Simplifying Fractions' 'Converting from Fractions to Percentages to Decimals', and 'Calculating the increase in Percentage (L2)' which better reflect the context in which percentages, fractions and decimals can be learnt and related to each other and to other numerical operations such as multiplication and division. The skill of any tutor is to be able to identify themselves areas of weakness that learners may have and to dovetail into and focus on those areas. The purpose of the methods outlined earlier is to give the learner the tools to solve everyday numeracy problems.

This can be followed by carrying out a learning assessment. The purpose of the learning assessment is to develop a grounding in numeracy up to level one, and act as a base or platform for developing skills beyond L1. It focuses on developing everyday numeracy skills and gives learners the opportunity to learn from the assessment itself, including from their own mistakes.

It also focuses on common areas of difficulty that many learners face. It attempts to go straight to those areas of difficulty and offers practical methods for solving problems. It's based on practical experience built up over recent years working with a range of learners in a range of educational environments (including work-based learning and further education colleges) and reflects success in using such methods and resources with those learners.

The learning assessment itself then is fully contextualised and consists of a part A and a part B.

Part A focuses mainly on the reading and interpreting of graphs, charts, tables and scales, and reading large numbers. Particular areas of difficulty include, for example, learners being able to:

- Interpret numbers in the hundreds of thousands (Q3) i.e. moving from 5 figures (tens of thousands) to 6 figures (hundreds of thousands).
- Know the axes of a graph and what their units are (Q5)
- Read scales which rise in increments of 2 (Q9)
- Understand exactly what the question is asking (Q1, 2, 5 and 11)

Although the focus of part A is not on calculations, questions 1 and 2 require the learner to interpret then add and subtract numbers from a tally chart and pictogram. Whilst Q1 can be carried out by subtracting without borrowing, Q2 can be carried out by borrowing. Alternatively, the learner can solve the problem by adding up from the lowest number to the highest number. Like all the other contextualised questions in the learning assessment, the learner needs to be able to understand what the question is asking before solving it. In question 1 for example, learners may find it difficult to find the busiest and quietest days, or appreciate that the morning and afternoon tallies need to be added or to understand the format of the question i.e. 'How many more... than...' This also applies to Q11 (Timetable) which many learners find particularly tricky. Here, learners should be encouraged to read (and if necessary re-read) the question carefully. Understanding the question can be particularly challenging for ESOL (English for Speakers of Other Languages) students, who may otherwise have good numeracy skills. As such, I would argue that the learning assessment is particularly useful for them too. Issues relating to the literacy of students, including ESOL students, are dealt with in detail in 'Making Britain Literate'.

Part B (which is accompanied by guidance notes) focuses more on calculations and relates directly to the methods outlined earlier.

Particular areas of difficulty in part B include, for example, learners being able to:

- use division in context to calculate fractions and average (Q14,15,16)
- calculate percentages (Q18,19,20)
- form and simplify a fraction (Q21)
- convert from fractions to percentages to decimals (Q13, 21)
- remember the formulae for calculating area and volume (Q23, 24)
- multiply decimals to calculate costs and use multiplication to calculate area and volume (Q22, 23, 24)
- round up/down to the nearest whole number and tenth (Q26, 27)
- multiply numbers by 10, 20, 30 etc (Q25, 30)
- convert from grams to kilograms and from metres to kilometres (and vice-versa) (Q30)

The learning assessment reflects an integrated (or holistic) approach to learning numeracy. For example, learners are steered towards a method for forming a fraction (1 part out of 5 as $\frac{1}{5}$ or 20 out of 80 as $\frac{20}{80}$), simplifying the fraction ($\frac{20}{80} = \frac{1}{4}$), converting the fraction to percentages ($\frac{1}{4} = 25\%$), relating fractions to division (to find a quarter of a number, you need to divide that number by 4), calculating 10% as the same as dividing by 10 (10% is 10 out of a 100 $= \frac{1\theta}{10\theta} = \frac{1}{10}$), showing the method for this and contrasting with multiplying by 10 and so on.

By carrying out calculations on paper (part B), the setting out of those calculations together with the workings can be shown and types of error identified and corrected. There would be no reliance on multiple choice or guesswork, and relevant methods for solving the calculations can be related (if the learner chooses) to methods outlined in guidance notes. Naturally if a learner produces correct answers using any alternative method that they are familiar with, or is able to solve problems mentally, then that would be fine. Having said that, if any method is either long winded and/or time consuming (and hence more prone to errors), then clearer, more straightforward methods should be offered. I have often found myself attending numeracy workshops whereby the facilitator has highlighted the number of different methods that can be used for mathematical operations such as multiplication and subtraction etc.

However, an issue often raised by parents with regards the way maths is taught to their children is that 'things are done differently now than when I was at school.' A lack of consistency with tried and tested methods over the years is, I believe, partly to blame for poor numeracy skills within the nation at large and for the inability of many parents to help their children at school.

A case in point would be to compare and contrast the use of the lattice method for multiplication with the method shown in the learning assessment for solving one of the problems:

Q25 A part-time catering assistant earns £6.15 an hour. How much does he earn for 30 hours work?

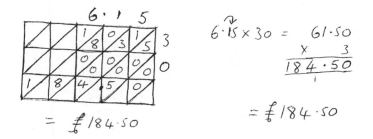

As can be seen, the lattice method (on the left) is more unwieldy, time consuming and complicated, and hence more prone to error. Furthermore, the website bbc.co.uk/skillswise describes the method as 'a bit complicated.' In some respects also, the lattice method can constrain a learner's numeracy development or instinct. For example, I have come across learners who, when asked to calculate the area of a strip of land which is 20m by 0.5m, start drawing out a grid, yet when I ask them what half of 20 is, they appear surprised that I've asked such a straightforward question!

The range of methods outlined in the guidance notes can serve to either remind or reinforce what learners know or teach them straightforward methods that they may not have been aware of. The questions in the learning assessment are contextualised, and the methods for solving problems focus on promoting everyday, functional numeracy skills. In writing out calculations (in part B), learners will, to a degree, need to come out of their 'comfort zone', but this will assist them in achieving their L1 adult numeracy (or key skills L1 application of number) test. Furthermore, in marking and providing feedback to the learner, experience can be gained by the tutor in identifying and correcting types of errors made by learners. As such, the tutor would have the opportunity to be more actively engaged with their learners' numeracy skills than is the case with the paper-based or laptop initial assessments and would be able to provide the learner with a good platform (in the form of a working document) from which any tutor could continue to support the learner should they require further support.

What I am arguing is that learners should not be put through any initial assessment unless they have been first given the opportunity to learn, whether it's learning a method for the first time or having previous learning reinforced.

The document would act as a diagnostic tool in showing areas of difficulty encountered, and degree of support required by the learner, with the added advantage of providing solutions to those areas of difficulty. The support can be given in the form of further L1 practice questions reflecting the weak areas and learner's needs. These will help to reinforce the relevant methods in particular areas. Having carried out calculations for themselves during the learning assessment, learners should be better placed to tackle such exercises and hence be better prepared for the L1 adult numeracy (or L1 functional skills mathematics) test.

Through having methods explained and illustrated, followed by having the opportunity to read through guidance notes and to carry out exercises themselves whereby they can utilise those methods, a range of the learner's learning styles are utilised and learning is reinforced.

I believe that a learning assessment would provide an opportunity for any organisation to replace existing initial and diagnostic assessments (paper-based and/or computer-based) with one practical, contextualised assessment which would both develop learners' everyday numeracy skills and assist tutors in supporting their learners.

As a final point here, I believe also that as well as for adult learners who struggle with numeracy, the L1 numeracy learning assessment would be suitable for use during years 7 and 8 of secondary school, where teaching and learning would be guided by their use as a formative assessment during those two academic years.

For learners who need to achieve L2 adult numeracy/application of number, the L1 learning assessment (along with the accompanying practice questions) acts as a good platform from which to move onto more advanced (L2) numeracy. The purpose of the L2 learning guide then is to assist the learner in developing those skills gained in the L1 learning assessment.

If we look at the following question from the L2 learning guide (Q7 from Calculations involving multiplication on P68) for example, we can see how the methods illustrated in the earlier pages, with regards conversions and choosing the most appropriate method to solve problems, can be used:

A gardener who maintains a lawn wishes to replace the topsoil. If the lawn measures 22m by 15m and the depth of the topsoil is 20cm calculate the volume of the topsoil.

Volume of topsoil = length x width x height

Length = 22m   Width = 15m   Height (or Depth) = 20cm = 0.2m = 1/5m

Volume = $22 \times 15 \times \dfrac{1}{5}$

$15 \times \dfrac{1}{5} = \dfrac{15}{5} = 15 \div 5 = 3 \quad 22 \times 3 = \mathbf{66}\text{m}^3 \quad$ or $\quad 22 \times \dfrac{\cancel{15}^{3} \times 1}{\cancel{5}^{1}} = \mathbf{66}\text{m}^3$

Alternatively, Volume $= 22 \times 15 \times 0.2$

$15 \times 0.2 = (10 + 5) \times 0.2 = (10 \times 0.2) + (5 \times 0.2) = 2 + 1 = 3 \quad 22 \times 3 = \mathbf{66}m3$

In the above case, I would argue that the first method i.e. converting 20cm to a fraction $\left(\dfrac{1}{5}\right)$ of a metre is the more appropriate method.

When this question is set for learners however, many instinctively (assuming they know the correct formula for calculating volume), begin by multiplying 22 by 15. The correct answer may be arrived at through multiplying the result (330) by $\frac{1}{5}$ or 0.2 correctly, but this would clearly, compared with the above method, be going about the problem in a roundabout way. In the event that learners are able to convert the 20cm to a fifth of a metre, or 0.2m then they still may not be able to multiply fractions and/or decimals (as outlined in the calculations above).

Interestingly, I have tried this out with a number of tutors too; the tendency is for them to also instinctively start to multiply 22 by 15 by whichever method they feel to be most suitable, en route to obtaining the answer. The purpose then of demonstrating a quicker, more direct method to tutors, is to try and develop a numeracy 'instinct', based on integrating a conversion into the calculation, which can in turn be put across to their learners.

In the context of a diagnostic assessment, a learner failing to answer the above question would/could be diagnosed as not being able to calculate 'Volume', whereas the problem could relate to any number (or a mixture) of areas, including:

- Not knowing the correct formula for calculating volume
- Not being able to multiply whole numbers
- Not being able to convert from centimetres to metres
- Not being able to multiply fractions
- Not being able to multiply decimals

Furthermore, on the basis that diagnostic assessments (whether paper or computer–based) tend to offer multiple choice answers, there is no way of knowing which (or how many) of the above areas the learner has difficulties with. It would also be possible for the learner to obtain the correct answer but by using long-winded and inefficient methods, and hence not learning any quicker, alternative methods.

The advantages, again, of learning assessments are that the opportunities to learn from worked examples are given, the tutor is able to see what methods their students use to solve problems, the type of errors (if any) that they make can be seen and corrected, and practical advice can be given on to how solve such problems.

Referring back to the above example, many learners lack the ability, and confidence, to convert comfortably and quickly from one unit to another as appropriate. Methods of solving problems through integrating conversions can be further developed through practice examples such as the following:

Example 1

A carpenter wishes to fix together 12 pieces of wood in a straight line. If each piece of wood is 80cm long, then calculate the total length of the wood.

$$12 \times 80cm \ = \ \begin{array}{r} 120 \\ \times\ 8 \\ \hline 960 \\ \scriptstyle 1 \end{array} \ = \ 960cm \ = \ \mathbf{9.6m}$$

$$80cm = \frac{4}{5}\ m \quad 4 \times 12 = \frac{48}{5} \ = \ 5\overline{\smash{\big)}48.^30}^{\,09.6} \ = \ \mathbf{9.6m}$$

80cm = 0.8m 0.8 × 12 = (0.8 × 10) + (0.8 × 2) = 8 + 1.6 = **9.6m**

$$0.8 \times 12 = 0.8 \times 10 \times \frac{12}{10} \ = \ 8 \times 1.2 \ = \ \begin{array}{r} 1.2 \\ \times\ 8 \\ \hline 9.6 \\ \scriptstyle 1 \end{array} \ = \ \mathbf{9.6m}$$

In this last example, we are multiplying (and dividing) by 10 (which cancel each other out) in order to create a more straightforward sum to solve.

I believe it would be good practice to work through each of the above methods with learners (even if they have a preferred method), on the basis that they reinforce each other, and give learners a wider range of methods to draw upon in solving numeracy problems in general.

Example 2

In this example, the ability to convert from one unit to another is integrated into a scale/ratio question:

On a scale drawing, two villages are shown as 4.5cm apart. If the drawing is to a scale of 1 : 200,000 then calculate the actual distance between the villages.

Scale is 1 : 200,000   or   1cm : 200,000cm

100cm = 1m   so,   200,000cm = 2,000m

1,000m 1km   so, 2,000m = 2km

Therefore, 200,000cm is equal to 2km

So, the ratio can now be written as 1cm : 2km and it follows (by doubling both sides) that: 2cm : 4km
            and   4cm : 8km

Also, as 1cm on the scale drawing represents an actual distance of 2km, then 0.5cm represents 1km   Therefore, 4.5cm : 9km

So, the distance between the 2 villages is **9km**

Example 3

A cupboard has the following dimensions:

Height = 2.0m Width = 1.2m and Depth = 0.6m

A man wishes to store as many boxes as possible in the cupboard. If the dimensions of the boxes are as follows, then calculate the maximum number of many boxes that could be stored in the cupboard:

Height = 30cm Width = 40cm and Length = 50cm

The boxes would need to be aligned in such a way so as to maximise the number that can be stored. To see how this can be done, we need to ensure that the dimensions of the cupboard and box are in the same unit.

So, looking at the dimensions of the cupboard:

Height = 2.0m = 200cm Width = 1.2m = 120cm and Depth = 0.6m = 60cm

200cm	120cm	60cm
4	3	2
50cm	40cm	30cm

So, 4 boxes will 'fit in' from bottom to top, 4 will 'fit in' going across and 2 will 'fit in' from the front to the back.

To work out the total number of boxes then, we need to multiply the three numbers:

4 x 3 x 2 = **24 boxes**

An issue learners often have with this type of question is that, in appreciating that the question relates to 'Volume', they start calculating the volume of the cupboard and/or box with a view to working the number of boxes that can be fitted into the cupboard. This is clearly impractical and long-winded.

In each of the above examples, there is an opportunity to develop the numeracy instinct in learners (referred to earlier).

A further advantage of the L1 numeracy learning assessment and the L2 numeracy learning guide, is that they lend themselves to the forthcoming L1 and L2 functional skills tests (which, at the time of writing, are being trialled across the country) through reflecting the areas/topics covered in the standards and providing guidance, through methods, to answer questions and spaces (where relevant) to show calculations. Functional skills will replace the current key skills and are set to form part of the new national diplomas for 14 – 19 year olds when they are rolled out nationally in September 2010. The 'coverage' and 'range' in the functional skills standards however do not contain 'calculating percentages' at any of the given levels.

In summary here then, the L1 learning assessment together with the L2 and L3 learning guides have been laid out in such a way that the vast majority of learners, (whatever their background or starting point) who struggle with numeracy, shown the relevant methods in the context of high expectations and enthusiasm, and given the time and support, could progress and achieve at a far higher level then they are currently at. The effect that this would have on learners' confidence levels would be immense as could be the potential knock on effect it could have on their job prospects in light of greater transferable skills and hence their (and society's) economic well being as a whole.

Although I haven't done it yet, I think I am stating the obvious when I say that calculators should not, and indeed need not, be used in any of the calculations covered at L1 or L2 (unless perhaps to check an answer). One of the problems in schools is the fact that students learn how to use a calculator before they have the numeracy skills to carry out the level of calculations outlined. Reliance on calculators prior to having those skills does I believe hinder the development of their numeracy. However, I've included a L3 numeracy learning guide, 'Going Further', in which the use of a calculator is needed. The purpose of the L3 numeracy guide is to develop skills gained from the L1 learning assessment and the L2 learning guide, and to assist learners in gaining a L3 numeracy qualification.

I often hear it said that learning maths should be fun. The problem with this point of view is the underlining assumption that the way maths is taught by the person putting forward this point of view both works and is fun at the same time, and that if you disagree, you believe maths should be boring and are some kind of killjoy. It's true that many people who struggle with numeracy, and certainly the vast majority of learners I work with for a variety of reasons really didn't like maths at school and still retain that dislike and fear of the subject. Comments and opinions often given include things like 'we just had a succession of maths teachers who didn't really care' or 'I hardly ever bothered turning up to maths lessons' or 'I was just given a calculator and told to get on with it' or 'I just couldn't do it'. However, the idea that maths should be fun is, I believe, subjective and missing the point that the main focus should be on making numeracy as straightforward as possible in order that it can be understood. Of course enjoyment or having fun while you're doing it is a bonus, but numeracy can only really be enjoyed to any extent once you've mastered it to an adequate degree.

I have often found whilst attending workshops, meetings or seminars etc. the main focus of which has been the issue of improving learners' maths skills, that the introduction of new types of technological resources, from CDs to new interactive websites etc. arouse people's interest, and are often warmly received. However, whilst appreciating the role of web-based technology and interactive smart boards etc and utilising such technology myself in supporting the development of learners' numeracy skills, I find that technological innovations can get a disproportionate amount of attention at the expense of issues such as raising the standards and expectations of learners and tutors, and the methods and strategies required for doing so. A case in point would be the reliance on technology in the administering of on-line diagnostic assessments which, in my opinion, lessens the need for tutors to interact with, and make judgments on, the numeracy skills of the learner (as alluded to earlier), hence leading to the deskilling of both tutor and learner i.e. by being able to rely on such technology, the need for the tutor to have advanced skills themselves, along with the expectations on them, is much reduced, and similarly, the process of sitting at a computer and clicking on this and clicking on that, in itself, does little to enhance a learners' numeracy skills. As a general point here, I would argue that the increased use of, and development in, technology over recent years has not met with a concomitant rise in the numeracy (or literacy for that matter) skills of our learners, and that whilst the use of technology in the classroom can, and does have further potential to, enhance learning, increased dependence on it could, I believe, on the contrary, end up being a further barrier to learning.

As mentioned earlier, a learner's schooling and home environment are major factors in their numeracy development. In terms of home environment, factors include parental support along with their ability to support, and the degree to which children are exposed to numerical concepts during their childhood development, for example through playing games requiring counting and developing spatial awareness through playing with building blocks and construction toys etc. It's difficult of course in the amount of time available with learners, and due to the potential sensitivity of asking questions relating to home environment, to ascertain the degree to which these may be factors in the development of the learner's numeracy skills. What can be assumed though is the greater the lack of home support and the poorer the learner's schooling was, then the greater will be the degree of compensatory support required for that learner.

However, the question needs to be asked, 'If they can learn numeracy as an adult, then why weren't they able to learn it while at school?' Unless they have a specific disability such as dyscalculia (symptoms of which include; distinguishing between digits; sequencing problems; understanding and remembering numerical terminology; directional difficulties relating to number operations and retaining information) that has been diagnosed, then I believe there is no excuse for allowing students to pass through school without having had the opportunity throughout their schooling to grasp the basics up to level 2 through consistent and thorough teaching and reinforcing of basic methods. Learning in schools needs to be organised to the degree whereby by the end of year 7 (i.e. at the end of the first year in secondary school), all children (excluding those with specific learning disabilities) are able to carry out calculations at a L1 standard and show L1 competence in terms of numerical knowledge, and should be able to cope with the L2 calculations well before leaving school at the current leaving age of 16.

In spite of the, 'Key conclusions' stated in the afore-mentioned report (Working on the 3 Rs), which outline the importance of, and need for, numeracy skills in the workplace, it could be argued that in the context of the changing job market over time (for example the decrease in the number of jobs in the manufacturing sector and the increase in the number of jobs in the service sector) along with the increased use of technology in employment, that there has been a decline in the need for numeracy skills to support those jobs. To an extent this may be true, but it also presupposes that those who do not achieve academically will end up in areas of employment and types of jobs where on the one hand there is a limited need for numeracy skills and yet on the other, there is limited scope for progression without those skills. Nevertheless, job roles are fulfilled, buoyed by strata of unemployed people below them and more skilled and qualified (or better connected) people above them.

This could in part explain why schools and the educational establishment have been able to get away with allowing many people to leave school and enter employment not prepared with basic numeracy skills and why there has been a perceived 'dumbing down' of standards and failure to solve the issue of innumeracy within a large proportion of society. Furthermore, whilst the report makes it clear that employers are dissatisfied with the level of numeracy skills of school leavers, it doesn't suggest methods by which employers may, in anticipation of their potential (or current) employees' possible low numeracy skills, test (and develop) their skills within the recruitment process or support their current employees in developing their numeracy skills.

I read with great interest, an article by Blacklock (2009: 10) in 'The Daily Express' recently in which a haberdasher lamented the fact that 9 out of 10 potential employees needed to be turned away at interview on the basis that they weren't able to do fairly basic sums or mental arithmetic without the use of a calculator. It was explained in the article that the manager of the haberdashery expected his employees to do simple sums in order to be able to 'calculate customers' bills' (either mentally or on paper) but that he found that '... failing education standards and over-reliance on calculators' had 'killed off many people's mental skills.' I take my hat off to the haberdasher for raising this issue. By taking a stance, the haberdasher has shown that he has high expectations of his employees. If other employers took a similar stand with regards their employees numeracy skills relative to their job role, then this could, I believe, potentially have a knock on effect on schools to ensure that maths is delivered in such a way that all their pupils are functionally numerate before they leave school. This can be achieved if they have high expectations of their pupils. However, it is clear from many people's direct and indirect experience and from research evidence, that millions of people have left (and are still leaving) school not functionally numerate. Unfortunately, this low level of expectations that exists in many of our schools continues into the further education sector in FE colleges and training providers. It shows itself, on the one hand, through the 'dumbing down' of course requirements in numeracy to the extent whereby to achieve a vocational apprenticeship, only evidence of level 1 numeracy achievement is required (level 2 in the case of advanced apprenticeships) and on the other hand, through the fact that tutors are recruited within the FE sector who, whilst having responsibility for their learners' numeracy skills, are not themselves able to demonstrate proficient numeracy skills, let alone the ability to deliver the necessary numeracy skills to others.

So, what defines whether or not someone is numerate? Is it someone who (without the aid of a calculator) can add up the cost of their groceries, calculate their pay, work out the percentage discount for an item in the sales, read a timetable, work out the shared cost of a restaurant bill, or convert from one currency to the other? In my opinion, it is someone who can work comfortably and confidently at level 2, i.e. with the questions in the level 1 numeracy learning assessment and level 2 numeracy learning guide.

As a quick fire way of determining a person's numeracy skills, I advocate the setting of the following numeracy challenge. I'm doing so in the context of an adamant belief that all school pupils and students studying in the further education sector (excluding those with specific learning disabilities) are capable of solving such problems and should be expected to do so. It sets, along with the L1 numeracy learnrning assessment, and L2 and L3 numeracy learning guides, a minimum standard that all teachers and tutors (in primary schools and within the FE sector) should comfortably be able to work to. As any teacher knows, it is a mistake to say something is easy, whether it's adding 3 and 2 or carrying out differential equations, since, as is quite obvious, something is only easy if you know it. However, what I can say, with reference to the 15 million or so people who have difficulties with numeracy, is that it is easy to put measures in place that would substantially reduce that number.

On February 17th 2010, I attended a presentation entitled 'Maths Education' at the Royal Society in Albermarle Street (which is, ironically, at the other end of the street from where the publishing company for this book used to be located). The main presenter was a maths professor from Sussex University, who espoused the virtues of 'investigative maths', based on research she had carried out in the United States, but there was also a panel of guests including a couple of celebrities (Carol Vorderman and Sanjeev Bhaskar) and a science professor from the Institute of Education (where, incidentally, I did my PGCE in integrated science). Following the presentation, questions were invited from the audience of several hundred people. One fairly astute member of the audience questioned why it was that children in China and India, who had, in general, received a more traditional maths education, whereby the learning of methods from the teacher took precedent over learning through 'investigative' methods, generally had a higher level of mathematical skills than their British and American counterparts!

I jotted down a few questions of my own, which I planned to ask; this included a question relating to language barriers to developing numeracy skills and what they thought were the effects of the use of the calculator on the learning of numeracy methods. Other questions I had lined up for the panel then related to the perceived decline of standards in maths and science qualifications, combined with the perceived lower levels of expectations of students' abilities and of the required mathematical skills of teachers. I don't know what I was thinking, expecting to ask so many questions, especially considering the fact that I'm prone to getting jittery in these situations, and stumbling over my words. Anyway, 10 to 15 minutes into the questions, the facilitator saw my raised hand from the back of the lecture hall and walked up the steps towards me with the microphone. I managed to blurt out my question relating to language, and got as far as the one on calculators, at which point, and upon seeing, I think, several further questions on the paper in front of me, the microphone was whipped away from me and the panel was asked to comment on the use of calculators, the issue of language being overlooked. A range of views was given by the panel varying, as one would predict, from advocacy and justification, to criticism, of their use. A little later, a question was raised by a member of the audience, relating to the amount of maths within Science GCSEs. The questioner asked how it had come to be, starting from approximately ten years ago, that the amount of maths contained in science GCSE qualifications had been substantially reduced. He gave an example relating to 'Moments' and how questions now tended to be based on whether a mass should be moved nearer or further away from the fulcrum to balance the other side rather than having to actually calculate the distance, mass or size of the Moment.

The Royal Institute has had many great speakers, including Michael Faraday and Marie Curie; apparently, the radiation emitted from one of her experiments can still be detected! I couldn't help wondering what they would think of the average level of scientific knowledge and mathematical skills of people in this country now, and how many are excluded from ever engaging in, or even being aware of, anything they'd achieved in science through a lifetime of research, discovery and innovation.

As stated earlier, in November 2009, an OFSTED report carried out by its Chief Inspector (Christine Gilbert) warned that in some schools, its pupils were being held back by its teachers' poor grasp of maths and science. This state of affairs begs a couple of quite straightforward questions. Why do potential employees or teachers not have their maths and science skills and knowledge tested at interview, and are those interviewing in a position to judge?

In the academic year 2010/2011, functional skills were rolled out across education providers as an essential element in the four qualification routes for young people from 14 to 19; in apprenticeships, GCSE, in the new Diploma, and the Foundation Learning Tier, as well as being stand-alone qualifications in their own right. They are regarded by Government as the core elements of English, mathematics and ICT that provide young people and adults with the skills and abilities they need to participate effectively and independently in life, learning and work, and have been introduced in order to address employers' concerns that young people and adults have not been achieving a firm enough grounding in the basics.

It is generally understood, and expected, in teaching that those who are delivering a particular subject should themselves be well qualified in that subject, and at the very least, be one level above the students they are teaching. However, during my experience in the post-16 sector, I have observed that many of the tutors delivering functional skills maths do not have a level 3 examined maths qualification. Furthermore, in terms of the entry requirements onto post-compulsory teacher training courses (Cert Ed or PGCE), it is my understanding that there is no minimum numeracy (or literacy) level entry requirement for trainee teachers, although there is meant to be a requirement to achieve a level 2 numeracy qualification by the end of the training. However, this can be achieved by passing a 40 question multiple choice level 2 adult numeracy test with 19 marks! In some cases, trainee teachers obtain their Cert Ed without even passing this qualification!

To deal with the competition in the job market within the context of today's economic climate, I've heard reports of employers demanding that in order to get on an apprenticeship programme, applicants need to have 4 good GCSEs (i.e. grades A – C), including maths and English, in order to be considered. It seems rather odd to me then, that in order to get onto a teaching programme, the bare minimum level of English and maths is not required (i.e. a level 2 GCSE 'equivalent' qualification), yet in order to be considered for an apprenticeship programme, GCSEs in both maths and English are becoming necessary!

I have argued on many occasions, over a period of years, that any tutor delivering numeracy should themselves have a level 3 numeracy qualification and that a level 2 numeracy qualification should be part of a stringent admissions policy for teachers entering the post-16 sector, and that that qualification should either be a GCSE in maths (grade A – C) or a level 2 functional maths qualification (but not a less rigorous level 2 adult numeracy qualification.

The issues raised above don't just happen though; standards, and the expectations of learners', and teachers, numeracy levels don't just decline, and as such, the context in which they have, needs to be reflected on. People have opposed the decline in standards, and called for higher expectations of learners and teachers. In meetings within a variety of educational establishments and at various levels, decisions to reduce the need for numeracy methods to solve scientific problems, to allow tutors to deliver numeracy to a level they barely have themselves, and to allow teachers onto, and to complete, teacher education courses with a low level of numeracy skills have all been opposed. Such decisions, I believe, have been as important as the methods and strategies in determining the fate of learners' numeracy levels in this country. My understanding is that the pass rate for level 2 functional skills maths across the country during the academic year 2010/2011 was less than 50%, and that is in spite of the running of functional skills 'pilots' for two years prior to the 2010/2011 academic year. I believe that the results speak for themselves, and that the correlation between poor results, the low level of expectations of learners' and tutors' numeracy skills and the methods and strategies deployed to assess and address their needs is evident.

The focus of the functional skills level 2 numeracy questions (as with many of the other questions throughout the book) is to encourage learners to engage in everyday aspects of numeracy, and in so doing, the range of methods and strategies to solve numeracy problems. The questions reflect the type of real-life, topical questions that are set in level 2 functional skills maths tests. The questions also take into account the amount, and level, of reading required, to answer questions in such tests, and reflect the need for learners to be able to interpret, extract and utilise relevant information from a range of topical, real-life data sources.

The questions take into account, and reflect concern from, a recent NIACE report which recommended '... *a system of measuring competence in applying mathematical concepts in real-life numeracy activities.*' The report states that '*one example of a relevant task might be equipping adults to assess whether the cost of travel to a supermarket further away, which claimed to have lower prices, would wipe out any savings*' (See question 4a, which is just such a task). The questions focus on everyday, real-life areas such as:

On-line shopping; energy bills, alternative energy costs; fuel costs and fuel efficiency; internet research; parts of a payslip (deductions, allowances, pension etc); interpreting data tables; reading, and drawing, graphs and scale drawings; unemployment statistics; the Olympic Games; population growth; equal opportunities; information contained on food labels; the energy contained in food; plotting and interpreting Body Mass Index etc.

The Numeracy Challenge

Q1. If a man earns £6.75 per hour, then calculate how much he would earn in a 37 hour week.

Q2. Calculate 13.5% of £250.00

Q3. Calculate the volume of concrete used in the construction of an industrial warehouse floor, which has the following dimensions:

Length = 25m   Width = 12m   Depth = 300mm

Q4. If the cost of 1.5kg bag of rice is £2.20 then calculate the cost of 400g of that rice

Q5. If the exchange rate between the Euro and the pound is: 1 Euro = £0.91 then calculate how many Euros (to the nearest cent) you would get from £70.00

Q6. The thickne ss of the ten pence piece is being increased in January 2011 from 1.7mm to 1.9mm. Calculate the percentage increase in the thickness of the coin (to the nearest whole number).

For methods and answers, see pages 55, 59–60, 69–70, and 103–105.

References

Blacklock M (July 11th, 2009) in *The Daily Express*, p10

CBI (2006) *Working on the Three Rs*, London: DfES

Curtis P (September 24th, 2008) in *The Guardian*, p4

Leitch review (2006) *Prosperity For All In The Global Economy*, Norwich: HMSO

Moser C (1999) *Improving Literacy and Numeracy – A Fresh Start*, Sudbury: DfEE

Smithers R (January 31st, 2006) in *The Guardian*, p1

L1 Numeracy Learning Assessment

Name: ....   **Date:** ....

The learning assessment consists of a Part A and a Part B. The guidance notes relate to Part B, and if necessary, are there to assist. You can refer to them as you carry out your assessment. If required, a tutor may guide you through them prior to you carrying out the assessment.

The purpose of the assessment is to check any weak areas you may have, but more importantly to give you the chance to learn from it, and to develop everyday numeracy skills. Following the assessment, a tutor will mark and give you feedback on it. The focus will then be on learning from errors, carrying out corrections and having them remarked.

The time allowed is flexible. As a guide, 10–15 minutes reading time, followed by up to 40 minutes for the assessment.

Part A

Tally Charts

	Morning	**Afternoon**
Monday	‖‖‖ ‖‖‖ ‖‖‖ ‖‖‖ ‖‖‖	‖‖‖ ‖‖‖ ‖‖‖ ‖‖‖ ‖‖‖
Tuesday	‖‖‖ ‖‖‖ ‖‖‖ ‖‖‖ ‖‖‖ III	‖‖‖ ‖‖‖ ‖‖‖
Wednesday	‖‖‖ ‖‖‖ ‖‖‖ ‖‖‖ ‖‖‖	‖‖‖ ‖‖‖ ‖‖‖
Thursday	‖‖‖ ‖‖‖ ‖‖‖ ‖‖‖ II	‖‖‖ ‖‖‖ ‖‖‖ ‖‖‖ I
Friday	‖‖‖ ‖‖‖ ‖‖‖ ‖‖‖ ‖‖‖ III	‖‖‖ ‖‖‖ ‖‖‖ ‖‖‖ ‖‖‖ III

Q1 The above tally chart shows the number of customers using a sports centre's new Bistro during its first week of opening. How many more customers used the Bistro during the busiest day than during the quietest day?

....

Pictograms

January	🌫🌫🌫🌫🌫
February	🌫🌫🌫🌫🌫🌫
March	🌫🌫🌫🌫
April	🌫🌫🌫🌫🌫
May	🌫🌫🌫🌫🌫
June	🌫🌫🌫🌫🌫🌫🌫

Key: 🌫 = 50 mobiles

Q2   The above pictogram shows the number of mobile phones sold by a retailer during the first six months of 2007. How many more mobile phones were sold in June than in January?

....

Reading and Interpreting Large Numbers

Q3   It was estimated that two hundred and one thousand, nine hundred and twenty six people attended a football match. Write this number on the line below:

....

Q4   During a recent 'Save the Earth' charity concert, 23 064 tickets were sold on-line. Write 23 064 in words on the line below:

....

Graphs

The bar chart shows the speed (in miles per hour) of five different
land animals:

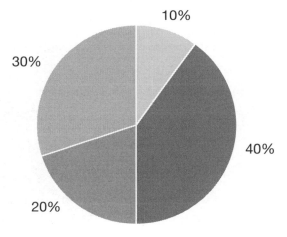

Q5 What are the units shown on the vertical axis?

....

Q6 According to the bar graph, how much faster is the jackal than the
pig?

....

Q7 A pie chart is often used for showing proportions. However, what is
missing from the following?

....

**Proportions of vehicles (cars,
buses, lorries and motorbikes)
which currently use the
motorways.**

Reading Scales

Q8 What is the weight shown on the following scale?

80kg   100kg   120kg

Q9 What is the measurement (in degrees Centigrade) shown on the following thermometer?

0°C   20°C   40°C

Rounding up/down

Q10 84,648 people attended a football match. How many is this to the nearest thousand?

Timetable

Q11 The following timetable shows the times of trains from Leighton Buzzard to London Euston:

Leighton Buzzard	9.43	10.13	10.43	11.13
Berkhamsted	9.53	10.23	10.53	11.23
Hemel Hempstead	10.03	10.31	11.03	11.31
Watford	10.11	-	11.11	-
London Euston	10.31	10.48	11.31	11.48

A man decides to take a train from Berkhamsted to London Euston some time between 10.00 am and 11.00 am
What is the difference in the times taken by the two possible trains he can catch?

Time

Q12 A woman leaves home at twenty five past eight in the morning. It takes her twenty five minutes to cycle to the station, following which she queues up for ten minutes to buy her ticket. She then waits a further ten minutes for her train to arrive. What time does her train arrive?

....

Part B

Converting fractions to percentages to decimals

Q13 Complete the following Fractions/Percentages/Decimal Conversion Table:

	Fraction	Percentage	Decimal
	1/2 (a half)		
		25%	
			0.75
		20%	
	2/5 (two fifths)		
		60%	
			0.8
		33%	

Division

Q14 A quarter of the spectators at a golf tournament were women. If there were 220 spectators, then how many of them were women?

Q15 A man decides to save two thirds of his tax refund towards a holiday. If his refund is £180.00 then how much does he save?

Calculating average

Q16 Six teams of engineering students take part in a rowing competition. The times were recorded by a timekeeper:

	Team 1	Team 2	Team 3	Team 4	Team 5	Team 6
Time (mins)	21	29	16	22	19	25

What is the average (mean) time recorded by the timekeeper?

Calculating range

Q17 In the above example, calculate the range of times for the 6 teams in the rowing competition.

Calculating 10% of a number

Q18 There is a 10% discount on a new computer. If its normal price is £782.00 then how much is the discount?

Calculating 5%, 20%, 30% etc of a number

Q19 In a survey of 700 people carried out by a new energy company, 20% said they were considering changing supplier. How many people is this?

Q20 Annual membership of a leisure centre normally costs £110.00. As part of a promotion, the centre is offering a 30% reduction for those who join before the end of January. How much will annual membership cost with the 30% reduction?

Forming a fraction, simplifying it, then converting it to a percentage

Q21 30 contestants enter a reality TV show. After one month, there are just 6 contestants left. What percentage of the contestants are left?

Multiplying decimals

Q22 A man buys 4 muffins at £1.15 each and 2 cappuccinos at £1.80 each. How much does he spend in total?

Calculating area

Q23 A gardener wants to measure the area of a flower bed. If the length is 7m and the breadth 1.5m then what is its area?

Calculating volume

Q24 An airline passenger concerned about hand luggage restrictions at airports, measures his case to be 40cm long, 10cm wide and 30cm high. Calculate its volume.

Multiplying by 10, 20, 30 etc

Q25 A part-time catering assistant earns £6.15 an hour. How much does he earn for 30 hours work?

Rounding up/down to the nearest whole number and to the nearest tenth

Q26 A man runs a 100m in 11.147 seconds. What was his time to the nearest tenth of a second?

Q27 The length of a warehouse is measured as 28.62m. What is the length of the warehouse to the nearest metre?

Ratios

Q28

A chef decides to try out a new recipe, 'Buttered Mussels', and uses the following ingredients:

3 cloves of garlic
70g of unsalted butter
½ lemon
a dash of tabasco
5 tablespoons of finely chopped parsley
3kg of mussels
3 finely chopped shallots
150ml of dry white wine

If the recipe is for 6 people, then how many grams of butter will he need for 24 people?

Scale drawings

Q29

The distance between 2 towns on a scale drawing is measured as 7cm. If the drawing is drawn to a scale of 1cm : 3km then what is the actual distance between the 2 towns?

Kilograms/kilometres

Q30

If a small loaf of bread weighs 400g, what would be the weight (in kilograms) of 40 loaves of bread?

Guidance Notes

Converting fractions to percentages to decimals

Make a note of the number of shaded parts, and the total number of parts for each pie chart. The fraction will be the number of shaded parts out of the total number of parts.

For example, 1 shaded part out of 5 parts in total = $\frac{1}{5}$ (a fifth).

Division

In order to calculate $\frac{1}{3}$ (a third) of a number, you need to divide that number by 3.

Worked example:

A bar manager carries out a smoking survey on 42 of her regular lunchtime customers, and finds out that a third of them are smokers. How many of the customers are smokers?

A third of 42 = 42 x $\frac{1}{3}$ = $\frac{42}{3}$ = $3\overline{)4^12}$ ^{14}

14 of the customers are smokers

In order to calculate $\frac{1}{5}$ (a fifth) of a number, you need to divide that number by 5.

Worked examples:

a) Five friends go out for a meal in a restaurant. The bill at the end of the evening comes to £110.00 The friends decide to split the bill equally. How much does each friend pay?

A fifth of £110.00 = $5\overline{)1\,1^10.00}$ $^{022.00}$ So, each friend pays £**22.00**

b) Two fifths of the passengers on a bus are children. If there are 60 passengers on the bus, how many of them are children?

To work out $\frac{2}{5}$ of 60, we can work out $\frac{1}{5}$ of 60, and then double it.

So, $\frac{1}{5}$ of 60 = $5\overline{)6^10}$ ^{12} Then, 2 x 12 = 24

So, **24** of the passengers are children.

Calculating the average of a group of numbers

Division is used to calculate averages:

Worked example - The weight of 6 patients was recorded by a nurse:

	patient 1	patient 2	patient 3	patient 4
Weight(kg)	79	75	79	63

To calculate the average weight of the patients, we need to add up all the weights (total), and divide by the number of patients (number).

So, average $= \dfrac{\text{Total}}{\text{number}} =$

$$
\begin{array}{r}
79 \\
75 \\
79 \\
+\ 63 \\
\hline
296 \\
\tiny 2
\end{array}
\qquad
296 \div 4 = 4\overline{)29^16}\ ^{74}
$$

So, the average (mean) weight of the patients is **74 kg**

Calculating the range of a group of numbers

To calculate the range of weights recorded by the nurse, we look for the highest weight and the lowest weight, then work out the difference between them.

So, range = highest number – lowest number = 79 – 63 = **16kg**

Calculating 10% of a number

Percent means out of a hundred.

So, 10% means 10 out of a hundred, which can be written as $\dfrac{10}{100} = \dfrac{1}{10}$ (a tenth)

In order to calculate $\dfrac{1}{10}$ (or 10%) of a number, you need to divide that number by 10.

To divide a number by 10, you make the number 10 times smaller by changing the place value of the numbers. For example:

$£24.50 \div 10 = \dfrac{£24.50}{10} = £2.45 \quad £8.90 \div 10 = £0.89 \quad £65.00 \div 10 = £6.50$

Calculating 5%, 20%, 30% etc of a number

In order to calculate 5% of a number, you can find 10% of that number and then halve it. For example:

This week only: 5% off your dry cleaning bill !

Calculate the discount on a usual bill of £24.00

10% of £2⌢4.00 = £2.40

5% of £24.00 = £1.20

In order to calculate 20% of a number, you can find 10% of that number (as above), and then double it. For example:

20% off our Chartered Flights!
Usual Price: £280.00

Calculate the discount:

10% of £28⌢0.00 = £28.00

20% of £280.00 = £28.00 x 2 = **£56.00**

In order to calculate 30% of a number, you can find 10% of that number and then treble it. For example:

30% off trainers!
Retail Price: £45.50

Calculate the sale price of the trainers:

10% of £4⌢5.50 = £4.55

30% of £45.50 = £4.55 x 3 = £   4.55   Sale price =   £4⁴5¹⁴.⁵5¹0
x   3   − £13. 6 5
                             _____   _____
                              13.65   **£31. 85**
                               ‾1‾‾1‾

Forming a fraction, simplifying it, then converting it to a percentage

Worked example:

> During a survey carried out into the eating habits
> of 80 young people, it was found that 20 of
> them described themselves as vegetarian. What
> percentage of the young people are vegetarian?

So, 20 out of the 80 young people are vegetarian:

20 out of 80 $= \dfrac{20}{80}$

We can simplify this fraction, since 20 will go into 80 (4 times) and into itself (once).

So, $\dfrac{\mathbf{20}^{1}}{\mathbf{80}^{4}} = \dfrac{\mathbf{1}}{\mathbf{4}} = \mathbf{25}\%$ (see conversion table)

Calculating area

To calculate the area of a rectangular space (e.g. the floor of a room), we need to multiply its length by its width: Area = length x width

Worked example:

A garden is 7m long and 4.5m wide. Calculate its area.

Area = length x width = 7m x 4.5m =

$$\begin{array}{r} 4.5 \\ \times\ \ 7 \\ \hline \mathbf{31.5}\ m^2 \\ \hline {\scriptstyle 3} \end{array}$$

Calculating volume

To calculate the volume of a cuboid shape (e.g. a room in a house, or a box), we need to multiply its length by its width by its height:

Volume = length x width x height

Worked example:

The kitchen in a restaurant is measured by a builder, and is found to be 8m long, 6m wide and 2.5 m high. Calculate its volume.

Volume = length x width x height = 8m x 6m x 2.5m

When you have to multiply 3 numbers together, it's best to multiply 2 of them together first, then multiply the result by the third number.

So, $\begin{array}{r} 2.5 \\ \times\ \ 6 \\ \hline {\scriptstyle 3}\ \ 1\,5.0 \\ \hline {\scriptstyle 4} \end{array}$ Then, 15 x 8 = $\begin{array}{r} 15 \\ \times\ 8 \\ \hline 120 \\ \hline \end{array}$ Answer = **120**m³

Volume is usually measured in m³, cm³, litres (L) or millilitres (ml).

Multiplying by 10, 20, 30 etc.

To **divide** a number by 10 we can do the following: £12.50 ÷ 10 = £1.25

To **multiply** a number by 10 we can do the following: £12.50 x 10 = £125.00

Further examples: £65.00 x 10 = £650.00 £4.05 x 10 = £40.50

To multiply a number by 20 we can multiply it by 10 and then double it:

Eg. A receptionist earns £5.25 an hour. How much does he earn for a 40 hour week?

£5.25 x 40 = £5.25 x10 x 4 = £52.50 x 4 =

$$£ \quad \begin{array}{r} 52.50 \\ \times \quad 4 \\ \hline £ \ \mathbf{210.00} \\ \hline {\scriptstyle 1\ 2} \end{array}$$

Rounding up/down to the nearest whole number and to the nearest tenth

A boy's weight is recorded as 46.362kg. What is his weight to the nearest kilogram?

tens	units		tenths	hundredths	
4	6	.	3	6	2

When giving an answer to the nearest whole number, there should be nothing after the decimal point. If the number after the decimal point (tenths column) is below 5, the number in the units column stays as it is.
So, answer = **46**kg

What is his weight to the nearest tenth of a kilogram?

When giving an answer to the nearest tenth, there should be just one number after the decimal point. If the number in the next column is 5 or above, the number in the tenths column is rounded up to the next number.
So, answer = **46.4**kg

Kilograms and kilometres

The word 'kilo' means a thousand. There are a thousand grams (g) in a kilogram (kg), and a thousand metres (m) in a kilometre:

1kg = 1,000g   2kg = 2,000g   0.5kg = 500g   2½kg = 2.5kg = 2,500g

1km = 1,000m   3km = 3,000m   0.6km = 600m   4.2km = 4,200m

The word 'cent' means a hundred. There are a hundred centimetres (cm) in a metre (m):

1m = 100cm   2m = 200cm   26m = 2,600cm   3.5m = 350cm   2.65m = 265cm

L1 Practice Questions

You will find while trying these questions, that the methods outlined in the L1 numeracy learning assessment, combined with a good knowledge of the times tables, should really help. As you become more familiar with the methods and the times tables, it should help speed things up for you and give you greater confidence in dealing with similar problems. Do not use a calculator!

1a T-shirts are on sale for £8.65 each. A man decides to buy 3 of them. How much does he pay?

1b Check your answer by dividing it by 3 and seeing if you obtain £8.65

1c If the man started off with £50.00 in his pocket, how much change will he have left?

2 A man receives his gas bill every 3 months. If his latest bill was £44.61 how much does that work out to be per month?

3 Three quarters of the residents of a care home are over 80 years old. If there are 36 residents in the care home, then how many of them are over eighty?

4 Five friends decide to club together to buy one of their friends a wedding present. If the present they have in mind costs £85.00 how much will they each have to put in?

5 The price of a regular latte was compared in 7 different venues and recorded in the table below:

	Venue 1	Venue 2	Venue 3	Venue 4	Venue 5	Venue 6	Venue 7
Cost (£)	2.30	1.70	1.85	2.25	1.85	2.60	2.15

5a What is the average (mean) price of a latte across the 7 venues?

5b In the above example, calculate the range of prices for a latte across the 7 venues.

6a Eight hundred and twenty people attend a concert. If two fifths of them are women, then how many of the people at the concert are women?

6b Check your answer by converting two fifths to a percentage, then calculating that percentage of eight hundred and twenty.

7 A traffic engineer monitors the traffic flow through a busy town centre. He records that out of 600 cars, 30% of them have sole occupancy (one person in the car). How many of the cars have sole occupancy?

8 3/5 of the mechanics working at a garage are on an apprenticeship programme:

a 3/5 as a percentage is written as: ....

b 3/5 as a decimal is written as: ....

9 It is predicted that soon, approximately 10% of books bought in this country will be bought online:

a 10% as a decimal is written as:..

b 10% as a fraction is written as:..

10 A man buys 30 litres of unleaded petrol at a garage. If the cost of unleaded petrol is 108.9p per litre, how much does he pay?

11 A pane of glass measures 2.2 m by 0.5 m. Calculate its area.

12 An interior designer measures the area of a living room, and works it out to be 42m². If the length of the living room is 7m then how wide is it?

13 The kitchen in a restaurant is measured by a builder, and is found to be 8m long, 6m wide and 2.5 m high. Calculate its volume.

14 A festival organiser employs 150 part-time workers for one day. If they each work 6 hours, and are paid £6.00 per hour, then what is the total amount paid for the workers?

15 A part-time receptionist at a sport centre is paid £6.20 per hour, and works 20 hours a week. How much does he earn in 4 weeks?

16 In an engineering class, there are 42 students. If 14 of the students are female, then what percentage of the students is female?

17 In a class of 15 students, it was found that 3 of the students had a learning disability. What percentage of the students had a learning disability?

18 Usain Bolt of Jamaica won the 200m gold medal at the 2008 Olympic Games in Beijing in a world record time of 19.30 seconds. If he broke the world record by two hundredths of a second (0.02 seconds), then what was the previous world record?

19 A tailor cuts 3.4m from a 20m length of cloth. How much does he have left?

20 A man leaves his house in the morning with £50.00 and spends £22.38 in his local leisure centre. How much money does he have left?

21 A couple are saving to put down a £36,000 deposit on a house. They have £23,350 saved. How much more do they need?

22 It was reported in a newspaper in August 2008 that there were 11.58 million pensioners and 11.52 million under-16s currently living in the UK. Calculate how many more pensioners there are than under-16s:

a as a number ....

b in words ....

23 In a children's playgroup, there is one child carer for every three children. If there are 18 children, then how many child carers are there?

24 A car is found, on average, to emit 300g of carbon dioxide into the atmosphere for every kilometre it travels. How many kilograms of carbon dioxide will it emit into the air during a 30km journey?

25 If a tin of baked beans weighs 400g, what would be the weight in kilograms of a case of 30 tins of baked beans?

26 A jogger records the distance she runs one morning as 4.05km. Calculate how many metres she has run?

27 A sandwich shop owner buys a 7.5m roll of kitchen foil in order to wrap his long baguettes. If he needs 50cm of kitchen roll to wrap each one, how many can he wrap with the 7.5m roll?

28 A man is training to take part in a cross-channel swimming relay, where each swimmer needs to swim 3.5 km. He trains in his local 'Olympic-sized' swimming pool which is 50m long. How many lengths would he have to swim during his training to reach 3.5km?

29 A man weighs himself and records his weight as 65.455kg. What is his weight to the nearest kilogram?

30 The length of a field is measured as 50.272m. What is the length of the field to the nearest tenth of a metre?

L2 Numeracy Learning Guide

Name: ....   **Date:** ....

This guide is intended to assist learners in developing their everyday numeracy skills. It builds on the skills gained (and the methods used) from the L1 numeracy learning assessment and contains worked examples and practice questions. It will also help learners to achieve a L2 adult numeracy (or L2 functional skills mathematics) qualification.

Forming and simplifying fractions

Worked Example:

A survey was carried out in a coffee shop to find out the popularity of different types of coffee.

Type of coffee	Number of people
Latte	87
Americano	44
Machiato	65
Espresso	68

Calculate the proportion of people who chose Americano as their favourite type of coffee.

Initially, we need to find the total number of people who took part in the survey. We can do this by adding up the numbers in the table.

$$\begin{array}{r} 87 \\ 44 \\ 65 \\ +\ 68 \\ \hline \mathbf{264} \\ \hline {\scriptstyle 2} \end{array}$$

Then, we need to form a fraction.

So **44** out of the **264** people who took part in the survey chose Americano as their favourite type of coffee.

44 out of 264 = $\dfrac{44}{264}$

We then need to simplify the fraction.

$$\frac{44}{264} = \frac{22}{132} = \frac{11}{66}$$

We can simplify further as 11 will go into the top and bottom:

$$\frac{\cancel{11}^{1}}{\cancel{66}^{6}} = \frac{1}{6} \quad \text{(a sixth)}$$

Questions – Forming and Simplifying Fractions

Q1 A new sports centre opens in Milton Keynes. The following table shows the number of visitors who used the different facilities during the opening hour of its opening day:

Facility:	Leisure pool	Table tennis	Badminton	Climbing wall
Number of visitors:	43	28	33	36

What proportion of the visitors played table tennis during the opening hour?

Q2 The following table shows the number of children who took part in a school's end of term activities:

Activity:	Number of Children:
Outdoor Sports	41
Indoor Sports	17
Board Games	20
Computer Club	41
Arts & Crafts	34

Calculate the proportion of children who chose indoor sports for their end of term activity.

Converting from fractions to percentages

To convert from a decimal (or fraction) to a percentage, we need to multiply the decimal (or fraction) by 100 so,

$$1/4 \times 100\% \ = \ \frac{100}{4} \ = \ 4\overline{)10^20} \ \begin{smallmatrix}2\,5\end{smallmatrix} \ = \ 25\%$$

$$1/5 \times 100\% \ = \ \frac{100}{5} \ = \ 5\overline{)100} \ \begin{smallmatrix}2\,0\end{smallmatrix} \ = \ 20\%$$

$$1/8 \times 100\% \ = \ \frac{100}{8} \ = \ 8\overline{)10^20.^40} \ \begin{smallmatrix}1\,2.\,5\end{smallmatrix} \ = \ 12.5\%$$

$$1/6 \times 100\% \ = \ \frac{100}{6} \ = \ 6\overline{)10^40.^40^40} \ \begin{smallmatrix}1\,6.\,6\,6\end{smallmatrix} \ = \ 16.7\% \quad \text{(to 1 decimal place)}$$

Converting from fractions to decimals

$\frac{1}{4}$ is one divided by four, $1 \div 4$ or $4\overline{)1.0^20}$ $\begin{smallmatrix}0.2\,5\end{smallmatrix}$ $= \ 0.25$

$\frac{1}{5}$ is one divided by five, $1 \div 5$ or $5\overline{)1.00}$ $\begin{smallmatrix}0.20\end{smallmatrix}$ $= \ 0.20$

$\frac{1}{8}$ is one divided by eight, $1 \div 8$ or $8\overline{)1.0^20^40}$ $\begin{smallmatrix}0.1\,2\,5\end{smallmatrix}$ $= \ 0.125$

In the worked example above, the simplified fraction was a sixth (1/6 or one part out of 6)

$\frac{1}{6}$ is one divided by six, $1 \div 6$ or $6\overline{)1.0^40^40^40}$ $\begin{smallmatrix}0.1\,6\,6\,6\text{'}\end{smallmatrix}$ $= \ 0.167$

Here, we can round up to 3 decimal places (3 numbers after the decimal point), so 0.1666' recurring becomes 0.167

Converting from decimals to percentages

0 . 2 5   x   100   =   25%

0 . 2 0   x   100   =   20%

0 . 1 2 5   x   100   =   12.5%

0 . 1 6 7   x   100   =   16.7%

Converting from percentages to fractions to decimals

Percent means 'out of a hundred'.

25%   = $\dfrac{2\,5\,.}{1\,0\,0}$ =   0.25

20%   = $\dfrac{2\,0\,.}{1\,0\,0}$ =   0.20

12.5.%   = $\dfrac{1\,2\,.\,5}{1\,0\,0}$ =   0.125

23%   = $\dfrac{2\,3\,.}{1\,0\,0}$ =   0.23

68%   = $\dfrac{6\,8\,.}{1\,0\,0}$ =   0.68

17.5%   = $\dfrac{1\,7\,.\,5}{1\,0\,0}$ =   0.175

Questions – Converting from fractions to decimals to percentages (and vice-versa).

Complete the following, 'Fractions/Percentages/Decimals Conversion Tables'

Complete the Fractions column first, then use the blank pages below to convert the fractions to decimals and percentages.

For the decimals column, give your answer to 3 decimal places (3 numbers after the decimal point). For the percentages column, give your answer to 1 decimal place (one number after the decimal point):

Fractions/Percentages/Decimal Conversion Table

	Fraction	Percentage	Decimal

	Fraction	Percentage	Decimal

Calculating percentages

When you calculate 10% of a number, you make the number 10 times smaller by changing the place value of the numbers. For example:

10% of £186.00 = £18.60 (See L1 learning assessment)

To calculate 1% of a number, the number is made 10 times smaller again:

1% of £1 8 6 . 0 0 = £1.86

Then, if we wish to calculate say 23% of £186.00 we can use the following method:

10% = £ 18.60   1% = £ 1.86

20% = £ 18.60   3% = £ 1.86
    x   2   x   3
   £ 37.20   £ 5.58
    1 1   2 1

So, 23% = 20% + 3% =   37.20
                +   5.58
                £ **42.78**
                  1

Worked Example:

VAT @ 17.5% needs to be added to a bill of £92.00. Calculate the VAT.

10% = £9.20   1% = £ 0.92   0.5% = £0.46

                7% =   0.92
                x   7
              £ 6.44
               1

17.5% = 10% + 7% + 0.5% =   9.20
                      6.44
                      0.46
                £ 16.10
                 1 1

Questions - Calculating Percentages

Q1 There are 900 men and women at a barbecue. If 57% of the people are men, then calculate the number of women at the barbecue.

Q2 A car is valued at £16,500.00. Calculate the cost of the car after VAT (@17.5%) has been added

Q3 Twenty three thousand six hundred people attend a free park concert. If 26% of them are children, then calculate the number of children at the concert.

Q4 In a recent survey, people were asked which of 6 cuisines (Indian, Chinese, Italian, Turkish, Mexican or Thai) they preferred. The results were presented in the following pie chart:

Pie chart (based on a survey) representing people's preferred cuisine

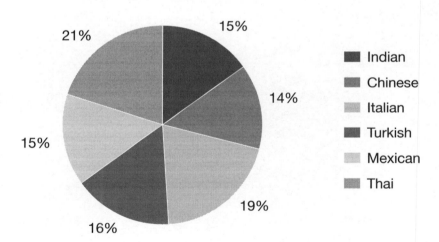

If 350 people took part in the survey, then calculate how many people chose Turkish as their preferred cuisine?

Calculating percentage increase (or decrease)

Worked example:

The table below compares electricity bills in 2006 with those in 2007 for 3 separate households:

	2006	2007
Household 1	£704	£880
Household 2	£675	£810
Household 3	£760	£798

Calculate the percentage increase in the cost of the electricity bills between 2006 and 2007 for each of the 3 households.

When calculating percentage increase, we can use the following method:

$$\frac{\text{actual increase}}{\text{original amount}} \times 100\%$$

So, for household 1, actual increase $= \begin{array}{r} 8^7 8^1 0 \\ -\ 7\ 0\ 4 \\ \hline 1\ 7\ 6 \end{array}$

$$\frac{\text{actual increase}}{\text{original amount}} = \frac{176}{704} = \frac{88}{352} = \frac{44}{176} = \frac{22}{88} = \frac{11}{44} = \frac{1}{4} \qquad \frac{1}{4} \times 100\% = \mathbf{25\%}$$

For household 2, actual increase $= \begin{array}{r} ^7 8^{10} 4^1 0 \\ -\ 6\ 7\ 5 \\ \hline 1\ 3\ 5 \end{array}$

$$\frac{\text{actual increase}}{\text{original amount}} = \frac{135}{675} = \frac{27}{135} = \frac{9}{45} = \frac{3}{15} = \frac{1}{5} \qquad \frac{1}{5} \times 100\% = \mathbf{20\%}$$

For household 3, actual increase $= \begin{array}{r} 798 \\ -\ 760 \\ \hline 38 \end{array}$

$$\frac{\text{actual increase}}{\text{original increase}} = \frac{38}{760} = \frac{19}{380} = \frac{1}{20} = \qquad \frac{1}{20} \times 100\% = \mathbf{5\%}$$

When calculating percentage decrease, we can use the following method:

$$\frac{\text{actual decrease}}{\text{original amount}} \times 100\%$$

Questions – Calculating percentage increase (or decrease)

The following bar chart compares the prices of 2 houses in a town in England between 2006 and 2007

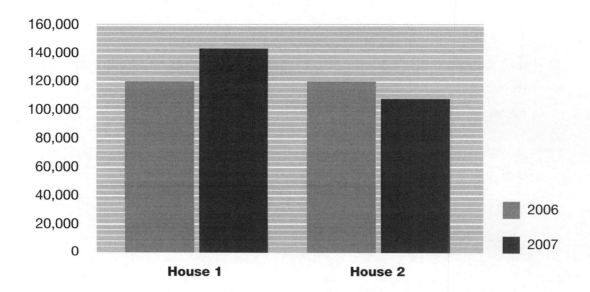

Q1a Calculate the percentage increase in the house price of House 1 between 2006 and 2007

Q1b Calculate the percentage decrease in the house price of House 2 between 2006 and 2007

Q2 In a recent bye - election, one of the main parties increased its vote from 12,500 to 16,250. Calculate the percentage increase in the party's vote.

$Q3$ A patient's temperature is recorded every 2 hours over a 12 hour period, and recorded in the table below:

Time:	8.00	10.00	12.00	14.00	16.00	18.00	20.00
Temperature (0C):	36.2	36.0	36.4	36.5	36.9	37.2	37.8

Calculate the percentage increase in the patient's temperature between 10.00 am and 8 pm

Calculations involving Multiplication

Worked examples:

1. A coaching assistant is paid £6.48 per hour. Calculate how much he earns in a 37.5 hour week.

£6.48 x 37.5

(37.5 = 30 + 7 + 0.5)

£6.48 x 30 = £64.80   £6.48 x 7 = £6.48   £6.48 x 0.5 = £3.24

$$
\begin{array}{r} \text{x} \quad 3 \\ \hline £194.40 \\ \hline {\scriptstyle 1\ 2} \end{array}
\qquad
\begin{array}{r} \text{x} \quad 7 \\ \hline £45.36 \\ \hline {\scriptstyle 3\ 5} \end{array}
$$

So, £6.48 x 37.5 = 194.40

$$
\begin{array}{r} 45.36 \\ + \quad 3.24 \\ \hline £\ \mathbf{243.00} \\ \hline {\scriptstyle 1\ 1\ 1\ 1} \end{array}
$$

2. A warehouse operative works 148 hours over a four week period. If she is paid £6.75 per hour, then calculate her pay over the four week period.

£6.75 x 148

(148 = 100 + 40 + 8)

£6.7 5 x 100 = £675.00   £6.75 x 40 = £67.50   £6.75
                                        x ___4   x ___8
                                       £270.00   £54.00
                                         3 2   6 4

So, £6.75 x 148 = 675
                  270
                + 54
                £999
                  1

Questions - Calculations involving multiplication

Q1 A barman is paid £5.85 per hour. Calculate how much he earns for a 36 hour week?

Q2 If the same barman works 8 hours overtime one Sunday, at time and a half, then calculate how much he earns on that Sunday.

Q3 A hotel receptionist works 42.5 hours in a week. If he is paid £6.00 per hour, calculate how much he earns in:

a) a week   b) four weeks

Q4a A chef is paid £6.30 per hour. If he works 175 hours in a month, then calculate how much he is paid for that month.

Q4b If the same chef works continues to work for the same amount of hours every month over the period of a year, then calculate how much he will earn in a year.

Q5 The diagram below shows a plan of 2 adjacent lawns.

Calculate their combined areas

Q6 Calculate the area of a warehouse which is 63m long by 22.4m wide.

Q7 A gardener who maintains a nearby lawn wishes to replace the topsoil. If the lawn measures 22m by 15m and the depth of the topsoil is 20cm calculate the volume of the topsoil.

Q8 If a tin of soup weighs 450g then calculate the weight of 33 tins of soup. (Give your answer in kilograms.)

Mean, Range, Median and Mode

A company director decides to carry out a survey relating to the age of the company's 14 employees. She records the following data in order to calculate the mean, range, median and mode:

Age of employees: 22, 31, 28, 18, 22, 31, 38, 31, 23, 26, 25, 24, 31, 28

Mean

The mean (or average) of a set of data is obtained by adding up all the individual pieces of data, and dividing the total by the number of pieces of data.

So, looking at the above data, the mean = 378 divided by 14

$$= 378 \div 14 = \frac{378}{14} = 14\overline{)3\,7^{9}8}\ \ \text{So, the mean} = \mathbf{27}$$

$$\begin{array}{r} 0\,2\,7 \end{array}$$

$$\begin{array}{r} 14 \\ \times\ \ 7 \\ \hline 98 \\ \hline {\scriptstyle 2} \end{array}$$

Range

The range of a set of data is obtained by finding the difference between the highest number and the lowest number within that data.

i.e. Range = highest number – lowest number = 38 – 18 = **20**

Median

The median of a set of data, is the number that occurs in the middle when the data is placed in ascending order.

18, 20, 22, 23, 24, 25, 27, 29, 30, 31, 31, 31, 31, 36

When there is an even number of pieces of data (in this case 14), then the median is the average of the two middle numbers (the 7th and 8th numbers).

So, looking at the above data, median = $\frac{27 + 29}{2}$ = **28**

Mode

The mode of a set of data is the number which occurs most frequently within that data.

Looking at the above data, **31** is the number that occurs most frequently (it occurs four times, which is more than for any other number in the data).

Questions - Mean, Range, Median and Mode

Q1 The following table records an airline's prices for flights from London to Madrid during a week in February:

Date:	4/2/08	4/2/08	5/2/08	5/2/08	6/2/08	6/2/08	7/2/08
Dep time:	9.30	16.45	7.40	16.30	9.30	16.45	7.40
Arr time:	13.00	20.15	11.10	19.55	13.00	20.15	11.10
Cost:	£43.00	£47.00	£43.00	£47.00	£43.00	£47.00	£43.00

Date:	7/2/08	8/2/08	8/2/08	9/2/08	9/2/08	10/2/08
Dep time:	16.30	9.30	16.45	7.40	16.30	7.45
Arr time:	19.55	13.00	20.15	11.10	19.55	11.05
Cost:	£53.00	£46.00	£56.00	£46.00	£61.00	£49.00

1a Calculate the average (mean) cost of the flights over the week.

1b Calculate the range of flight costs over the week.

1c Calculate the median cost from the above data.

1d Calculate the mode from the costs in the above data.

Ratios

We can use ratios to compare numbers.

Worked example:

546 people turn up at a local cinema for the opening night of the new, 'James Bond' film. Of these, 135 are men, 75 are women, 192 are boys and 144 are girls. Calculate the ratio of:

a) men to women

The ratio of men to women is 135 to 75 which can be written as 135 : 75 Like with fractions, we can simplify ratios by doing the same to both sides.So, for the ratio of 135 : 75 we can divide both sides by 5
Then, 135 : 75 becomes 27 : 15
We can simplify further by dividing both sides by 3
So, 27 : 15 becomes **9 : 5** (and this is its simplest form).

b) girls to boys

The ratio of girls to boys is 144 : 192 = 72 : 96 = 36 : 48
Both sides can be divided by 12 so, 36 : 48 becomes **3 : 4**

c) adults to children

The number of adults is
$$\begin{array}{r} 135 \\ + 75 \\ \hline 210 \\ \hline {\scriptstyle 1\ 1} \end{array}$$

The number of children is
$$\begin{array}{r} 192 \\ + 144 \\ \hline 336 \\ \hline {\scriptstyle 1} \end{array}$$

So, the ratio of adults to children is 210 : 336 = 105 : 168

Both numbers can be divided by 3 (we can tell this because if we add up the digits of each number, the sums are divisible by 3).

i.e. 1 + 5 = 6 (which is divisible by 3) and 1 + 6 + 8 = 15 (which is also divisible by 3)

So, 105 : 168 = 35 : 56

Both sides can be divided by 7, so 35 : 56 becomes **5 : 8**

Questions – Ratios

Q1 The following pie chart shows the proportion of people by sector studying for an apprenticeship with a work-based learning provider:

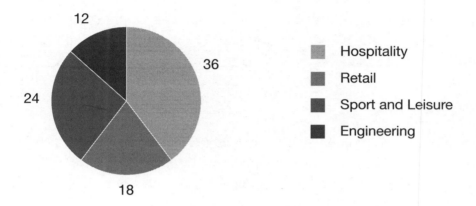

From the above data, calculate the ratio of apprenticeship trainees across the four sectors i.e. hospitality to retail to sport and leisure to engineering

Q2 Within the hospitality sector, the trainee apprentices are working towards the following NVQs;

Food and drink service (15)   Food processing (9)

Customer service (6)   Front of house (6)

From the above data, calculate the ratio of apprenticeship trainees across the 4 NVQs.

Q3 In a supermarket, the ratio of 'boxes of strawberries' to 'boxes of blueberries' sold in one day is 13 : 2
If there were 208 boxes of strawberries sold, then calculate the number of boxes of blueberries that were sold.

Q4 The following table shows the number of ascents made by climbers in 2006 on the world's five highest mountains:

Mountain:	Mount Everest	K2	Kangchenjunga	Lhotse	Makalu
Height of Mountain (ft):	29,035	28,250	28,169	27,940	27,766
Height of Mountain (m):	8,850	8,611	8,586	8,516	8,463
Number of ascents:	145	45	38	26	45

From the above data :–

a What is the ratio of the number of ascents that took place on the highest mountain to the number of ascents that took place on the second highest mountain?

b What is the ratio of the number of ascents that took place on the second highest mountain to the number of ascents that took place on the fifth highest mountain?

Level 2 Functional Skills Numeracy Questions

1 In an effort to support fair trading practices in developing countries, student A buys 18 bars of 'Fairtrade' dark chocolate with spices and orange oil.

a If each bar weighs 40g, then calculate the total weight (in kilograms) of the chocolate bars.

b If each bar contains 200 calories of energy, then calculate the total energy (in kilojoules) contained in the 18 bars (1 kilojoule ≈ 240 calories).

c The food label on each bar of chocolate shows the following information:

Fat	Saturated fat	Sugar	Salt
14.6g	9.2g	16.3g	trace

From the above information, calculate the percentage of saturated fat in each bar.

d For breakfast, the student decides to try out a new cereal. The food label on the packet of cereal contains the following information:

Each 30g serving contains:

Calories	Sugars	Fat	Saturates	Salt
114	5.1g	0.5g	0.2g	0.3g
6%	6%	<1%	<1%	6%

of the guideline daily amount.

From the above information, calculate the guideline daily amount of salt that people require.

e The packet also claims that the cereal contains less than 2% fat. Is this claim true? Show your workings.

f The student has her friends over for dinner and decides to cook Arancini (fried rice balls), an old Sicilian dish. She checks her recipe for the dish:

10ml of olive oil
half a small shallot, finely cut
1 clove of garlic, thinly sliced
60g carnaroli risotto rice
20ml white wine
300ml vegetable stock
    Gorgonzola
10g parmesan
    walnuts
20g plain flour
1 egg
20g white breadcrumbs
vegetable oil, enough to deep fry

However, her recipe for the dish doesn't show the amount of gorgonzola or walnuts. If the ratio of rice to gorgonzola to parmesan to walnuts to flour to breadcrumbs is:

12 : 8 : 2 : 3 : 4 : 4

then calculate the amount of gorgonzola and walnuts (in grams) that she needs for her recipe.

g   The following day, the student decides to check the information on the label of her bottle of olive oil:

Each 30g serving contains:

Calories	Sugar	Fat	Saturated fat	Salt
133	0g	15g	2.2g	0g
7%	0%	21%	11%	0%

of the guideline daily amount.

From the above information, calculate the approximate guideline daily amount of calories that people require.

h   Check if the guideline daily amount of calories, calculated for olive oil, works out to be the same as the guideline daily amount of calories shown on the food label for the breakfast cereal.

i   Whilst reading the Sunday papers, the student notices an article about the health benefits of olive oil, based on recent research. She reads that:

> 'People who cook with olive oil, add it to salads and dip their bread in it cut their risk of stroke by 41% once diet, exercise and weight are taken into account.'

She also reads the following:

> 'It is believed that regular use of olive oil could protect against conditions such as high cholesterol, high blood pressure and heart disease.'

Carry out some research into facts and figures associated with these claims.

j   Carry out some research into facts and figures associated with food groups and food labelling.

2   Student B receives his electricity bill and decides to check the calculations:

Cost of electricity you've used this period:

Night readings

10 Mar '11 – estimated   33092
18 Apr '11 – estimated   33434

$\quad\quad$ =   **(a)** kWh used over 40 days (estimated)

$\quad\quad$ **(a)** x 5.296p $\quad\quad\quad$ = $\quad\quad$ £ **(b)**

Day readings

10 Mar '11 – estimated 17531
18 Apr '11 – estimated 18024

$\quad\quad$ =   **(c)** kWh used over 40 days (estimated)

$\quad\quad$ **(c)** x 12.472p $\quad\quad\quad$ = $\quad\quad$ £ **(d)**

Total cost of electricity used = (b) + (d) = (e)

From the above information, calculate:

a   The estimated night reading (the difference between the readings on 18 Apr '11 and 10 Mar '11) in kWh.

b   The cost (to the nearest penny) of the electricity used at night between 10 Mar '11 and 18 Apr '11 (calculated as the number of Kilowatt Hours (a) x the price per unit (5.296p).

C The estimated day reading (the difference between the readings on
18 Apr '11 and 10 Mar '11).

d The cost (to the nearest penny) of the electricity used during the day
between 10 Mar '11 and 18 Apr '11 (calculated as the number of Kilowatt
Hours (a) x the price per unit (12.472p).

e The total cost of electricity used (b + d).

f The average cost (to the nearest penny) of the electricity used per day
over the 40 days.

Student B also receives the following information on his electricity bill:

If you continue to use energy at the same rate over the next 12 months,
we estimate your cost will be £537.60 based on the following tariff
breakdown:

Period	Your tariff	Projected cost
19 April '11 – 18 April '12	standard	£537.60

The cost of your electricity isn't just the price of your fuel:

5% Profit

12% Government obligation to help the environment

7% VAT and corporation tax

12% Operating costs

27% Delivery to your home

37% Wholesale electricity

g Calculate the estimated combined cost over the 12 months of the Government obligation to help the environment, and the energy supplier's operating costs.

h Calculate the difference in cost over the 12 months between the estimated price of the wholesale electricity and the estimated price of delivery to the student's home.

i An alternative energy supplier claims to be able to reduce the cost of student B's electricity bill. They offer a 15% reduction on the current energy supplier's projected cost. If, however, there is an eighty five pound transfer payment to be made for changing supplier, then calculate if the student would make a saving (in the year April '11 to April '12) by changing supplier.

In order to reduce his energy costs, as well as his 'Carbon Footprint', the student decides to buy some greener living, light 'Sticks'. In terms of the carbon output, the 'Sticks' produce 6.5kg of Carbon Dioxide per 1,000 hours of use compared with conventional 60W light bulbs, which produce 34kg of Carbon Dioxide per 1,000 hours.

From the above information, calculate:

j The approximate carbon output of the light 'Sticks' as a proportion of the carbon output of the conventional 60W light bulbs.

k   The amount of Carbon Dioxide that would be produced in a leap year by one light 'Stick' that was constantly on.

| Carry out some research into facts and figures associated with alternative energy sources.

3a   Students A and B are debating who has the most fuel efficient car. Student A states that her car, on average, does 420 miles on a full tank of 40 litres, whilst student B states that his car, on average, does 16km/litre. Which student has the more fuel efficient car?
(1 mile ≈ 1.6 kilometres)

b   Student B's car takes 12½% more fuel in its tank than student A's car. Calculate the amount of fuel, in gallons, that is needed to fill Student B's car.
(1 gallon ≈ 4.5 litres)

The two students decide to travel from their flat in London to Edinburgh for the weekend, with two of their friends, in the more fuel efficient car.

c   The car's Sat-Nav shows the distance to their destination in Edinburgh as 420 miles. One of the students decides to check this distance by making an estimation using a map. If the scale of the map is 1 : 2,000,000 and she measures the distance as 33 cm, then calculate the difference between the estimation and the Sat-Nav reading.

d The four friends decide to share the cost of the petrol equally. If the cost of petrol is 133.9p per litre, then calculate, to the nearest 10p, the cost of petrol that each of the friends have to pay.

Before the trip, one of the students decides to check on the weather report:

Weather Report for June 1st, 2011:

	Sun (hrs)	Rain (mm)	Temp (°C) High/low		Weather (noon)
Aberdeen	8.3	0.1	17	7	Showers
Aberystwyth	1.9	0.4	15	11	Cloudy
Aviemore	6.9	1.4	13	5	Showers
Barrow in Furness	4.9	0.6	15	11	Sunny
Belfast	5.3	1.4	14	9	Sunny
Birmingham	2.7	0.0	20	12	Cloudy
Bognor Regis	0.9	0.0	16	8	Cloudy
Bournemouth	1.4	0.0	17	12	Cloudy
Bristol	2.2	0.2	17	12	Rain
Cardiff	0.2	0.7	15	12	Rain
Cork	5.1	0.0	14	10	Cloudy
Cromer	3.2	0.0	19	12	Cloudy
Dublin	3.1	0.1	17	10	Sunny
Durham	3.1	0.0	17	9	Cloudy
Edinburgh	7.9	0.9	14	8	Showers
Eskdalemuir	5.0	6.2	13	6	Showers
Glasgow	7.9	4.6	13	7	Showers
Guernsey	0.4	0.0	15	12	Cloudy
Holyhead	0.8	0.1	15	12	Cloudy
Hove	2.2	0.0	16	13	Cloudy
Huntingdon	5.4	0.0	19	12	Cloudy
Ipswich	2.9	0.0	21	12	Cloudy
Isle of Mann	4.3	0.4	15	10	Sunny
Isle of Wight	1.0	0.0	14	12	Cloudy
Jersey	0.8	0.0	16	12	Cloudy
Kilkenny	4.7	1.2	14	7	Cloudy
Kinlochewe	5.4	17.5	11	7	Rain
Kirkwall	0.9	11.5	11	7	Cloudy
Leeds	3.2	3.4	17	10	Rain
Leuchars	8.9	0.0	16	7	Sunny
Liverpool	2.9	0.0	16	12	Cloudy

London	3.3	0.0	20	13	Cloudy
Malin Head	5.3	5.0	13	8	Cloudy
Manchester	0.3	0.5	16	11	Rain
Margate	7.6	0.0	20	12	Sunny
Morecambe	4.8	0.2	16	11	Cloudy
Nottingham	0.3	0.0	17	12	Cloudy
Okehampton	1.5	0.4	16	11	Cloudy
Oxford	4.5	0.2	17	12	Cloudy
Plymouth	5.6	0.3	15	12	Cloudy
Portsmouth	3.9	0.1	15	13	Showers
Prestwick	4.6	4.4	13	8	Showers
Shannon	3.8	0.9	14	11	Cloudy
Shrewsbury	1.8	0.0	16	12	Cloudy
Skegness	4.2	0.0	17	11	Cloudy
Southend	6.1	0.0	20	13	Sunny
Stornoway	3.5	6.8	11	6	Rain
Swansea	4.0	1.6	14	12	Cloudy
Tiree	0.0	2.6	12	8	Showers
Valentia	0.3	1.0	13	11	Fair

Sun & Moon

Sun rises: 04 52

Sun sets: 21 04

Moon rises: 03 11

Moon sets: 18 56

e Calculate the temperature range across the five capital cities shown in Britain and Ireland (i.e. London, Cardiff, Dublin, Belfast and Edinburgh).

f Calculate the average rainfall across the five capital cities.

g Which place, shown on the weather report, had the highest recorded temperature range?

h Which place, shown on the weather report, had the highest amount of sunshine?

i Calculate the amount of daylight there was on June 1st.

k One of the students is a keen athletics fan. He applies on-line for a ticket for the 100m men's sprint final in the London Olympics. Unfortunately, however, there are only thirty thousand tickets available and approximately one million people have applied. Approximately what percentage of those people applying for tickets on-line, will not be successful in their application for tickets for the 100m men's sprint final?

l Overall, one million and nine hundred thousand people applied on-line for tickets of their choice for the London Olympics. Of those, one million and two hundred thousand people were not successful in the ticket allocation the first time round. Those who were successful, on average, received 5 tickets each at a cost, again on average, of £75 a ticket. Calculate the income generated from the on-line sale of tickets, the first time round, for the London Olympics.

m Carry out some research into facts and figures associated with fuel prices.

n Carry out some research into facts and figures associated with climate change.

4 Student A usually cycles to her local supermarket (Safebury's) to do her shopping. However, she hears that a new supermarket (Morose) has opened up, approximately 8 miles from where she lives, which claims to offer better value for money for shoppers. She makes a list of typical items that she buys on a regular basis, and decides to compare prices:

Product	Supermarket	
	Safeburies	**Morose**
1 Litre of skimmed milk	£0.83	£0.86
2 x 1 litre cartons of orange juice	£1.75 per carton	£1.95 per carton
Broccoli (335g)	£1.27	£1.35
Organic spinach	£1.00	£1.10
Large wholemeal loaf of Bread (800g)	£1.36	£1.38
600g bag of apples	£1.67	£1.70
2 kg of bananas	35p/lb	35p/lb
1 kg of carrots	30p/lb	35p/lb
Peppered steak (435g)	£4.00	£4.00
Pork loin steaks (0.66kg)	£4.00	£4.00
Chicken (1.45kg)	£4.00	£4.00
Original coffee granules (200g)	£4.00	£3.85
Pure vegetable oil (1L)	£1.10	£1.25
Salted butter (750g)	£0.98	£0.94
12 free range medium eggs	£2.73	£2.80
Milk chocolate digestives	£1.00	£1.10
Easy cook rice	£1.06	£1.06
3 in 1 Shampoo	£2.20	£2.45
TOTAL		

(1 kg = 2.2 lb)

The following deals/offers at the supermarkets apply:

Safeburies:
1L Cartons of orange juice – 2 for £2.50

Morose:
1L cartons of orange juice – buy 1, get one free
Portions of peppered steak (435g), pork loin steaks (0.66kg) and chicken (1.45kg) - £4.00 each or any 3 for £10.00

Calculate:

a Calculate which of the two supermarkets would be more economical for student A to shop in (bearing in mind the cost of petrol used in driving to the Morose supermarket).

b The student notices that supermarkets up and down the country have checkouts which state '10 items or less.' Why is this statement incorrect?

c The student reads an article which states that in 2006, the average food shopping bill was 40% less than it is June 2011. If that's the case, then calculate what the student's shopping bill would have been at Safeburies in 2006.

d In order to attract more custom, both supermarkets decide to start an 'on-line' shopping option for its customers. They decide to start with the following offers:

Safeburies: 10% off any order above £30.00

Morose: 5% off any order above £30.00

Calculate, with the above offers, which of the two supermarkets would Student A's shopping have been cheaper on-line.

e Student A wants to update her mobile phone and decides to go on-line to check some Phone deals for the new AI Phone models:

AI Phone:				
Model A	**Model B**	**Model C**	**Model D**	
£5 a month for first 3 Months followed by £10 a month thereafter	First 3 months free followed by £15 a month	£15 a month with £50 cashback	£20 a month for first year followed by £10 a month for second year	Phones on a 24 month contract when you sign up on-line.
200 mins	300 mins	500 mins	600 mins	Mins to all UK Mobiles & UK Landlines (starting 01, 02,03)
500 texts	Unlimited texts	Unlimited texts	Unlimited texts	Standard UK texts
250MB	250MB	500MB	500MB	UK mobile internet a month

She wishes to obtain the best phone she can (in terms of memory and number of minutes per month), with unlimited texts, up to a maximum price of £350 over the two years. Which model should she choose?

f Carry out some research into facts and figures associated with on-line shopping.

g Carry out some research into facts and figures associated with mobile phone tariffs.

5 The following table shows the level 2 Functional Skills results for two groups of students:

Group 1

Student	Presentation	Discussion	Reading	Writing	Maths
Tommy Cooper	F	P	P	P	P
James Paxton	P	P	P	P	F
Harry Kamboni	P	P	P	P	P
Chris Parsloe	P	P	P	P	P
Robert John	A	P	P	F	P
Jennifer Kerans	P	P	P	P	F
Heather Slater	F	P	P	P	P
Nigel Osatch	P	P	P	P	F

Group 2

Student	Presentation	Discussion	Reading	Writing	Maths
Christine White	P	P	P	P	P
Ian Wall	A	A	P	P	P
Rob Harris	P	P	P	P	F
Simon Fudge	P	P	P	P	P
Peter Brightman	F	P	F	F	F
Neil Barney	P	P	P	P	P
Letchimi Nair	P	P	P	P	P
Kevin George	P	P	P	P	F
Steve McDaniel	P	P	P	F	P
Andrew James	P	P	P	P	P
Clive Dean	P	P	P	P	F

Key: P = Pass   F = Fail   A = Absent

a Calculate the fraction of students from the 2 groups combined who have completed all the requirements of the Functional Skills level 2 English (i.e. presentation, discussion, reading and writing).

b Calculate the difference between the percentage pass rate in maths between the two groups.

C Calculate the overall percentage pass rate in maths of the two groups combined.

d The maths resit is taken, and two more people pass, one from group A and one from group B. Calculate the new overall percentage pass rate in maths of the two groups combined.

e Carry out some research into facts and figures associated with GCSE and A-level pass rates over recent years.

The following table shows a comparison of the number of short-term and long-term unemployed people in the UK across three different age brackets, as recorded in May 2011:

UK Unemployment

		Short-term (Less than a year)	Long-term (More than a year)
18 – 24 years	Male	299,000	135,000
	Female	226,000	85,000
25 – 49 years	M	332,000	281,000
	F	328,000	155,000
50+ years	M	136,000	134,000
	F	79,000	50,000
Total	M	767,000	550,000
	F	633,000	290,000

f What is the ratio of the total number of short-term unemployed people to the total number of long-term unemployed people?

g In the 50+ age range, how many more short-term unemployed adults are there than long-term unemployed adults?

h In the 18 – 24 years old age range, how many more male unemployed adults are there than female unemployed adults?

Unemployment in the UK 1992–2011

Source: ONS

i From the above line graph, state, in words, the approximate difference between the level of unemployment and the claimant count in 2001.

j Carry out some research into facts and figures associated with levels of unemployment.

6 A new novel 'The Berlinesque' is released on to the market. The following data table shows the number of books sold per hour in a bookshop in the first week following its publication:

	Mon	Tues	Weds	Thurs	Fri	Sat	Sun	Total
9 – 10	1	0	4	3	1	5		
10 – 11	4	5	7	5	3	5	3	
11 – 12	4	6	7	8	5	4	4	
12 – 1	6	9	10	6	3	7	4	
1 – 2	5	8	9	9	8	9	8	
2 – 3	7	6	10	10	8	9	6	
3 - 4	8	3	8	9	8	6	4	
4 - 5	4	5	5	4	4	5		
5 - 6	6	5	9	8	7	6		
6 - 7				6	5	2		
7 - 8				4	3	3		
Total								

a From the above data, calculate:
The average number of books sold per hour on the first day of its sale.

b The average number of books sold per day.

c The average number of books sold between 1 and 2pm during the first week of its sale.

d The range of books sold per hour during the week.

e On which day the median occurred for the total number of books sold per day.

f The average number of books sold per hour on this day.

g During the second week of sales, 420 books were sold in the bookstore. Calculate the percentage increase (to one decimal place) in the number of books sold during the second week of sales.

h The books are stored in boxes (6 per box) which are 35cm long by 25cm wide by 20cm tall. The boxes are stored in a space in a warehouse which measures 1.4m long by 1.25m wide by 1.6m tall. Calculate the maximum number of books that can be stored in the space.

If the results shown in the data table were represented in a pie chart, then calculate:

i the number of degrees that Thursday's sales would represent (to the nearest whole number).

j the percentage of the pie chart that Monday's sales would represent on the pie chart (to the nearest whole number).

k   In the space below, draw a bar chart of the results in the data table
(days of the week along the X-axis, and total number of books sold per
day along the Y-axis).

l   In the space below, draw a line graph to compare the hourly book sales on
Thursday and Friday (hour intervals along the X-axis (9 - 10, 10 – 11 etc)
and number of books sold per hour along the Y-axis).

j   Carry out some research into facts and figures associated with the
increasing popularity of E-books.

7 New research shows that there are currently approximately 3.5 million home workers in the UK, and that approximately 60% of new businesses are started from home.

A business woman is considering setting up a business to support 'home-working' social entrepreneurs who require collaborative working office spaces to match their needs, as an alternative to working from home. As such, she is looking to rent some premises, and is considering the following three options:

Site A	Area = 48 m²	Rent per month = £420
Site B	Area = 42 m²	Rent per month = £360
Site C	Area = 54 m²	Rent per month = £468

a The woman chooses the site which offers the best value for money in terms of the cost per square metre.

She plans to charge her clients £20/day to use her office, for which they will have use of a shared desk area, together with wi-fi, and tea and coffee. She plans to open her office from Monday to Friday, and estimates, based on the interest shown by local entrepreneurs in her business, that on average six people per day will use the facilities.

Calculate how many weeks it will take before she is able to cover the cost of the annual rent i.e. 'break even.'

A plan is drawn of the office using a scale of 1 : 25

Below are some measurements and real life sizes of areas within the plan:

	DRAWING SIZE	REAL LIFE SIZE
Office area	(c) x (d)	7m x (b)
Comfy chair area	11cm x 9cm	(e) x (f)
Desk area (g)	(h) x (i)	4m x 1.5m
WC/bathroom	7cm x 5cm	(j) x (k)
Kitchen (7 m²)	(m) x (n)	(l) x 2m

Calculate the following:

b)

c)

d)

e)

f)

g)

h)

i)

j)

k)

l)

m)

n)

○ Carry out some research into facts and figures associated with changing property prices.

○ Using a scale of 1 : 50 draw a plan of the office (including comfy chair area, desk area, WC/bathroom and kitchen) in the space below:

8 On Thursday, May 5th, there was a referendum in the United Kingdom on the introduction of an Alternative Voting System in the country. Approximately nineteen million, two hundred thousand people of voting age voted in the referendum, the result being as follows:

32% in favour of the Alternative Vote (Yes campaign).
68% opposed to the Alternative Vote (No campaign).

Given the above result, calculate the following:

a The approximate number of people who voted in favour of the alternative voting system (to the nearest one hundred thousand).

b The number of people who opposed the alternative voting system (to the nearest one hundred thousand).

c If the turnout for the vote was roughly 42% of the population, then calculate the approximate number of eligible voters in this country (to the nearest one hundred thousand).

d If the current population of the United Kingdom is approximately 60 million, but is predicted to rise to 71 million by the year 2033, then calculate the percentage increase in the country's population (to one decimal place).

e In 2009, the estimated population of Britain was 61,113,205 and on June 15th 2011, it was estimated at 60,432,098 Based on these figures, calculate the reduction in the population of Britain between these times.

f   In April 2011, 30 million people in Britain had a Facebook account. However, by the end of May 2011, that number had decreased by 100,000 (as people apparently become bored with the site and concerns grow over privacy issues etc). If this decrease was to continue at the same rate (i.e. at 100,000 people per month), then calculate when the number of people with a Facebook account will have reduced by 10% from its peak of 30 million.

g   There are currently approximately 5,000 transgender adults living in Britain. Taking the adult population of Britain to be approximately 45 million adults, calculate how many non-transgender adults there are for every one transgender adult.

h   The black minority ethnic (BME) population of England is estimated as 11%. Taking the population of England to be 50,760,000, calculate the approximate non-BME population of England (to the nearest one hundred thousand).

i   The population of Bedford is approximately 80,000 If the BME population of Bedford is approximately 10,000 then calculate whether or not Bedford has a higher, or lower, than average BME population within England.

j   In Bedfordshire 14.3% of people have a disability, health problem or long-term illness. If the population of Bedfordshire is approximately 382,000 then calculate the approximate number of people in Bedfordshire who have a disability, health problem or long-term illness.

In 2009/10, there were an estimated 555,000 new cases of work-related ill health:

- Stress, depression or anxiety – 234,000 cases
- Musculoskeletal disorders (MSD) – 188,000 cases
- Other illnesses – 133,000 cases

In addition, the estimated number of injuries at work in the same year (which met the criteria to be reportable under the RIDDOR regulations) was 233,000

From the above information, using Microsoft Office Excel, create a pie chart showing the percentages of each of the four categories of Health and Safety incident (i.e. Stress, MSD, other illnesses and Injury), then sketch it in the area below:

Comparison of work-related incidents of ill health and injury – 2009/10

l   In 2009/10, there were an estimated 23.4 million working days lost as a result of work-related ill health:

- Stress, depression or anxiety – 9.8 million
- Musculoskeletal disorders (MSD) – 9.3 million
- Other illnesses – 4.3 million

In addition, there were an estimated 5.1 million working days lost in 2000/10 due to workplace injuries.

From the above information, using Microsoft Office Excel, create a pie chart showing the percentages of each of the four categories of working days lost due to work-related ill health and injury (i.e. Stress, MSD, other illnesses and Injury), then sketch it in the area below:

Comparison of days lost due to work-related ill health and injury – 2009/10

m   Scientists researching into human evolution have recently claimed that 30,000 years ago, Cro-Magnon man, the earliest modern human, had a brain volume of approximately 1,500 cubic cm. On the basis that the average brain size of man today is approximately 1,350 cubic cm, calculate the percentage decrease in man's brain size since Cro-Magnon man.

n   Find out the population of your home town. Has the population there been increasing or decreasing over recent years?

O   Find out the population of a country that you have visited or where a friend, or colleague of yours, is from. Has the population there been increasing or decreasing over recent years?

p   Whilst the actual number of substantiated cases of child abuse is not known, the approximate number of children in the UK known to be at risk is (i.e. those appearing on the child protection register). Find out this number. Also, find out the percentage of young adults who were severely maltreated during childhood.

q   Carry out some research on the internet into facts and figures associated with equal opportunities.

9   A college employee receive his payslip at the end of the month, only to find that parts of it are missing:

Organisation		**Employee Name**		**Employee Number**	
A1 College		Lucky Jim		012345	

Pay and Allowances		**Deductions**		**Period Details**	
Salary	2345.00	Income Tax	349.00	Date Paid	26/**(a)**/2010
Project Allowance	90.00	National Insurance	183.27	Tax Period	08
Travel-862 miles @ 40p/mile	**(b)**	Teacher's Pension (6.4%)	**(c)**	Tax Code	647L

National Ins No.
AB 12 34 56 C

PAYE Reference
123 D45678

Total Pay	**Total Deductions**	**NET PAY**
(d)	**(e)**	**(f)**

Annual Salary
(g)

From the above information, calculate:

a   The exact date the employee was paid (bearing in mind that the tax year begins in April).

b   The employee's travel allowance.

c   The employee's pension contribution.

d   The employee's total (or gross) pay (= Salary + Project Allowance + Travel Expenses).

e   The employee's total deductions (= Income Tax + National Insurance + Teacher's Pension).

f   The employee's net pay (Total Pay – Total Deductions).

g   The employee's annual salary (monthly salary x number of months in year).

h   Carry out some research into facts and figures associated with minimum pay rates and average earnings.

10 Examine the Body Mass Index (BMI) chart below:

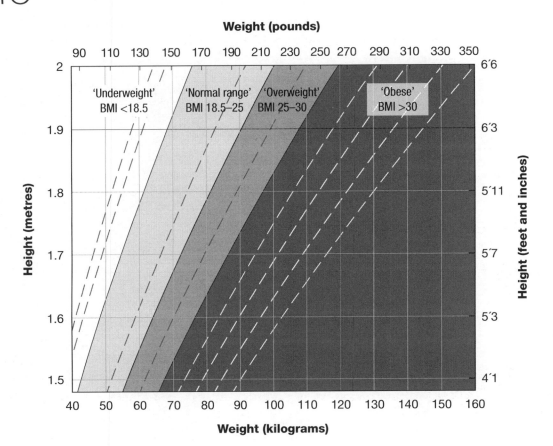

a Student D measures his height as 1.70m and weight as 90kg. Using the above table, plot the student's Body Mass Index, and state which category his BMI falls under (i.e. underweight, Normal Range, Overweight or Obese).

Body Mass Index can also be calculated using the following formula:

$$BMI = \frac{Body\ Weight\ (in\ Kg)}{(Height\ (in\ m))^2}$$

b Calculate Student D's BMI (to the nearest whole number) using the above formula, and check if it's in the same category as the value plotted on the BMI chart.

C Student C knows her height and weight in Imperial measurements. If her height is 5 feet and 9 inches, and her weight is 11 stone and 6 pounds, then plot her Body Mass Index on the above table, and state which category her BMI falls under.
(1 stone = 14 lbs)

d Plot your own Body Mass Index on the above chart.

e Calculate your Body Mass Index using the above formula, and check if it's in the same category as the value plotted on the BMI chart.

f Carry out some research into facts and figures associated with childhood obesity rates.

g The expression '20/20 vision' relates to a measurement of the clarity of eyesight. What do the numbers 20/20 actually mean though?

h What is the average blood pressure for a healthy adult? What do the numbers refer to?

i Find out your own blood pressure, and record your reading below. Is it high, average or low? Give an example of a high blood pressure reading and a low blood pressure reading.

j   How many teeth does an adult have? What are they types of teeth, and how many of each does an adult have? How many teeth make a complete set of primary (baby) teeth?

k   A high waist circumference (the distance around your abdomen) is associated with an increased risk of Type 2 diabetes, high cholesterol, high blood pressure and heart disease. Men shouldn't let their waist size go above what value (in inches). What is the value for a woman's waist size?

l   How much moderate exercise (in minutes) should adults take each day?

m   Lung capacity is measured in air flow as you breathe. What is the ideal peak flow for a healthy, non-smoking young man?

n   What is the unit used to measure noise, and what is its range?

o   What is the circumference of the earth (in miles, and kilometres) at the equator (to the nearest whole number)?

p   What is the average distance (in miles, and kilometres) between the earth and the moon?

q What is the distance (in miles, and kilometres) between the Earth, and Mars when it is nearest to the Earth?

r What is the average distance (in miles, and kilometres) between the earth and the sun?

s What is the speed of sound?

t What is the speed of light?

L3 Numeracy Learning Guide
(Going Further)

Name: ....

The following guide outlines a range of methods for solving numeracy problems at level 3. Its purpose is to develop skills gained from the L1 learning assessment and the L2 learning guide and has been put together to assist learners gain a level three application of number qualification. Read them through carefully, and try the practice questions at the end.

Conversions

As you look through level 3 application of number practice papers, you will see that within many of the questions, you need to convert from one unit to another. For example:

    with distance (kilometres to miles, or yards to metres etc)

    with speed (miles/hour to metres/second, or knots to miles/hour etc)

    with area (mm^2 to m^2, or square feet to square metres etc)

    with volume (gallons to litres, or m^3 to mm^3 etc)

    with money (Euros to Pounds, or pounds to Swiss Francs etc) and all vice-versa.

In each case you will be given the conversion (e.g. 1 Euro = 0.626 Sterling), it's just a case of using it correctly within the problem.

Worked examples

a) If 1 Euro = 0.626 Sterling, how much sterling (to the nearest penny) would you get for 226.3 Euros?

    226.3 x 0.626 = 141.6638 = **£141.66** (to the nearest penny)

    However, you could be given the amount of Sterling, and asked to calculate the amount of Euros.

    If 1 Euro = 0.626 Sterling, how many Euros (to the nearest Euro) would you get for £1010.58?

    1 Euro = 0.626 Sterling

If we divide both sides by 0.626, then $\dfrac{0.626}{0.626}$ Sterling = $\dfrac{1}{0.626}$ Euro

So, 1 Sterling = $\dfrac{1}{0.626}$ Euro = 1.597 Euro (to 3 decimal places)

Then, 1010.58 Sterling = 1010.58 x 1.597 Euro = 1,613.896 Euro = **1,614** Euros (to the nearest Euro).

b) If 1 mile = 1.6103 kilometres, then how many metres are run in a marathon, which is 26.2 miles?

1 mile = 1.6103 km So, 26.2 miles = 26.2 x 1.6103 km = 42.18986 km

1 km = 1000 m so to convert from km to m, you need to multiply by 1000. When you multiply by a thousand, you move the decimal point 3 points to the right.

So, 1.6103 km = 1,610.3 m

1 mile = 1,610.3 m 26.2 miles = 26.2 x 1,610.3 m= 42,189.86 m = **42,190 m** (to the nearest m)

c) One lap of a horse race is 1 mile and 1 furlong (there are 8 furlongs in a mile). If a horse runs 6½ laps in 20 minutes and 17 seconds, then what is his average speed in metres per second (to 3 decimal places)?

Average speed = distance travelled ÷ time taken = $\dfrac{\text{distance travelled}}{\text{time taken}}$

The answer needs to be in m/s, so we need to calculate the distance in metres and the time in seconds.

Distance = 6.5 x 1.125 miles (1 furlong = 1/8 mile = 0.125 miles) = 7.3125 miles

(1 mile = 1,610.3 m) So, 7.3125 miles = 7.3125 x 1,610.3 m = 11,775 m
Time = 20 mins and 17 secs = (20 x 60) + 17 = 1200 + 17 = 1,217 secs

So, average speed = $\dfrac{\text{distance}}{\text{time}} = \dfrac{11,775}{1,217}$ m/s = 9.675 m/s (to 3 d.p.)

d) A car is recorded driving along the A507 (where the speed limit is 60 miles/hour) at 26 metres per second. Is the driver breaking the speed limit?

We need to convert 26 m/s into miles/hour

1,610.3 m = 1 mile   So, $\dfrac{1,610.3 \text{ m}}{1,610.3} = \dfrac{1}{1,610.3}$ miles = 0.000621 miles

1 m = 0.000621 miles and 26 m = 26 x 0.000621 miles = 0.016146 miles

So, a speed of 26 metres per second = 0.016146 miles per second

In other words, the driver travels 0.016146 miles in one second

There are 3,600 (60 x 60) seconds in an hour, so in one hour the driver would travel

3,600 x 0.016146 miles = 58.1256 miles

The driver's speed is therefore **58.1256 miles/hour**, which is not breaking the speed limit.

e) The following diagram shows a lawn drawn to a scale of 1:250

37mm

65mm

Calculate the area of the actual lawn in square metres (to 2 d.p.)

Length of lawn = 65mm x 250 = 16,250mm = 16.25m (1m = 1000mm)
Width of lawn = 37mm x 250 = 9,250mm = 9.25m

Area = length x width = 16.25 x 9.25 = 150.3125 = **150.31m²** (to 2 d.p.)

f) The area of a circular pond is measured and found to be 51.38m²

If a scale drawing of the pond was made using a scale of 1:125 then what would the diameter of the pond be on the scale drawing (to the nearest mm)?

Area of circular pond = π r² = 51.38m² (π = 3.14)

so, 3.14 x r² = 51.38 and r² = $\frac{51.38}{3.14}$ = 16.363m and r = 16.363 = 4.045m

Diameter = 2 x radius = 4.045 x 2 = 8.09m

On a scale drawing of 1 : 125   8.09m would be shown as 8.09 ÷ 125 = 0.06472m

0.06472m = 64.7mm = **65mm** (to the nearest mm)

g) How many cubic millimetres (mm³) are there in 4.72 cubic metres (m³)?

First we need to calculate how many mm³ are in 1m³

1m = 1000mm (milli = a thousandth) and 1m³ = 1m x 1m x 1m

So, 1m³ = 1000mm x 1000mm x 1000mm = 1,000,000 x 1,000 = 1,000,000,000mm³

i.e. 1m³ = a thousand million mm³ or 1 billion mm³ and 4.72m³
= **4.72 billion mm³**

Writing very large and very small numbers in standard form

The moon is 384,400,000.0m from the earth.
This is a rather large and cumbersome number, so we can write it in what is called 'standard form'. We do this so that very large (or very small) numbers can be more clearly expressed and compared.

- Place the decimal point after the first digit (3.844), then look at how many places the decimal point has moved to the left (or how many places the digits have moved to the right)

- To compensate for each place moved, we need to multiply by 10. In this example, the decimal point has moved 8 places to the left, so we need to multiply the above number by 10, eight times (i.e. 10×10×10×10×10×10×10×10). We can express this as 10 to the power 8 (10^8) i.e. 10 multiplied by itself 8 times.

- The above number can now be written in standard form as **3.844 × 10^8**

- On a calculator, this can be inputted as **3.844** followed by **Exp** (which stands for 'exponential' or 'x 10 to the power of ...') followed by **8**

Looking at the numbers in the above example (g):

1,000,000 (1 million) = 1 x 10^6 or just 10^6 and 1,000,000,000 (1 billion) = 1 x 10^9 or 10^9

and 4,720,000,000 (4.72 billion) = 4.72 x 10^9

As well as very large numbers, we also need to work with very small numbers:

1 millimetre = 0.001m 1 micrometre = 0.000001m and 1 nanometre = 0.000000001m

The diameter of large bacteria is approximately 2 micrometres or 0.000002m

- Place the decimal point after the first digit (2.0), then look at how many places the decimal point has moved to the right (or how many places the digits have moved to the left)

- To compensate for each place moved, we need to divide by 10. In this example, the decimal point has moved 6 places, so we need to divide the above number by 10, six times i.e. $\dfrac{2.0}{10 \times 10 \times 10 \times 10 \times 10 \times 10} = \dfrac{2.0}{10^6}$

$\dfrac{1}{10}$ (or 0.1) can be written as 10^{-1}

$\dfrac{1}{10^2}$ (or 0.01) can be written as 10^{-2} and so on

- So, the above number can be written in standard form as **2.0 x 10^{-6}**

Also, 0.001m (1mm) expressed in standard form is 1.0 x 10^{-3} m

Percentages

The whole notion of percentages (like any other part of numeracy I guess) can cause confusion amongst learners. Before tackling any level 3 application of number question on percentages first ensure you are familiar with the methods outlined in the L1 numeracy learning assessment and L2 numeracy learning guide.

Year	1960	1970	1980	1990	2000	2007
Population of the world (in 1000s)	3,021,475	3,692,492	4,434,682	5,263,593	6,070,581	6,573,338

The above table shows the population increase of the world from 1960 to 2007

Calculate the percentage increase in the world population from 1970 to 2000

$$\% \text{ increase in population 1970 to 2000} = \frac{\text{increase in population}}{\text{Population in 1970}} \times 100\%$$

$$= \frac{6,070,581 - 3,692,492}{3,692,492} \times 100\% = \frac{2,378,089}{3,692,492} \times 100\% = \textbf{64.4\% (to 1dp)}$$

Trigonometry of a right angled triangle (i.e. Pythagoras, sine, cosine and tangent)

Pythagoras:

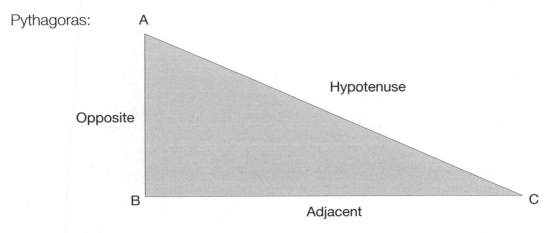

Pythagoras's theorem states that:

The square of the Hypotenuse is equal to the sum of the squares of the other two sides

In other words,   **$(AC)^2 = (AB)^2 + (BC)^2$**

So, if AB = 6.2cm and BC = 12.2cm,

then $(AC)^2 = (6.2)^2 + (12.2)^2 = 38.44 + 148.84 = 187.28$

$(AC)^2 = 187.28$ and therefore AC = $\sqrt{187.28}$ (the square root) = 13.69cm (to 2 dps)

Sine, Cosine and Tangent

Sine

For a given angle ACB, the ratio between the side opposite the angle and the hypotenuse is constant.

This ratio is called the Sine (Sin) of the angle and is equal to the opposite over the hypotenuse:

$$\text{So, Sin (ACB)} = \frac{\text{Opposite}}{\text{Hypotenuse}} = \frac{AB}{AC} = \frac{6.2}{13.69} = 0.453 \text{ (to 3 dps)}$$

If Sin (ACB) = 0.453 then angle ACB = 26.9° (to 1 dp)

Cosine

For a given angle ACB, the ratio between the side adjacent to the angle and the hypotenuse is constant.

This ratio is called the Cosine of the angle (Cos) and is equal to the adjacent over the hypotenuse:

$$\text{So, Cos (ACB)} = \frac{\text{Adjacent}}{\text{Hypotenuse}} = \frac{BC}{AC} = \frac{12.2}{13.69} = 0.891 \text{ (to 3 dps)}$$

If Cos (ACB) = 0.891 = then angle ACB = 26.9° (to 1 dp)

Tangent

For a given angle ACB, the ratio between the side opposite to the angle and the side adjacent to the angle is constant.

This ratio is called the Tangent of the angle (Tan) and is equal to the opposite over the adjacent:

$$\text{So, Tan (ACB)} = \frac{\text{Opposite}}{} = \frac{AB}{} = \frac{6.2}{} = 0.508 \text{ (to 3 dps)}$$

$$\text{Adjacent} \qquad \text{BC} \qquad 12.2$$

If Tan (ACB) = 0.508 = then angle ACB = 26.9° (to 1 dp)

Looking at the above examples, it might sound obvious, but it is important that you are familiar with how to use your scientific calculator.

Looking at Sine for example, you first work out 6.2 divided by 13.69 = 0.453

On my calculator then, I press **2nd F** followed by **sin⁻¹** followed by 0.453 to obtain the angle 26.9° (to1 dp)

Similarly, for cosine it's **2nd F** followed by **cos⁻¹** followed by 0.891 to obtain the angle

and for tangent it's **2nd F** followed by **tan⁻¹** followed by 0.508 to obtain the angle

In order to calculate angle BAC:

There are 180° in a triangle, so angle BAC = 180° − (90° + 26.9°) = 180 -116.9 = **63.1°**

Angle BAC could also be found by finding the sine, cosine or tangent of the angle.

In these cases however, relative to angle BAC, side BC would now be the opposite side, and side AB would be the adjacent side (with AC remaining as the hypotenuse):

$$\text{Now, Sin(BAC)} = \frac{\text{Opposite}}{} = \frac{\text{BC}}{} = \frac{12.2}{} = 0.891$$

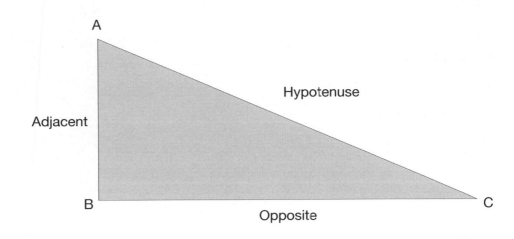

$$\text{Hypotenuse} \qquad \text{AC} \qquad 13.69$$

If Sin(BAC) = 0.891 then angle BAC = 63.1° (**2nd F** ; **sin⁻¹** ; 0.891)

And, $Cos(BAC) = \dfrac{\text{Adjacent}}{\text{Hypotenuse}} = \dfrac{AB}{AC} = \dfrac{6.2}{13.69} = 0.453$

If Cos(BAC) = 0.453 then angle BAC = 63.1° (**2ⁿᵈ F; cos⁻¹**; 0.453)

And, Tan(BAC) = Opposite = BC = 12.2 = 1.968

 Adjacent AC 6.2

If Tan(BAC) = 1.968 then angle BAC = 63.1° (**2nd F; tan⁻¹**; 1.968)

In some cases, the angle may be given, and one of the sides needs to be calculated:

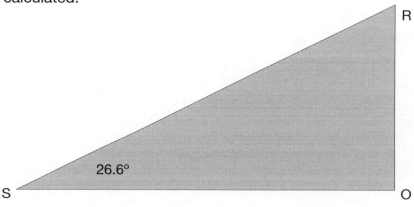

For example, a woman walks at an average speed of 0.9m/s for 1hr 17mins from village O to S then continues towards village R at the same speed. Calculate:

a) the distance from village S to village R in kilometres.

b) the total time taken if she carries on her journey, at the same speed from R back to O

a) From O to S, speed = 0.9m/s and time = 1hr 17mins
   (= 1.283hrs = 1.283 x 3600s)

$Speed = \dfrac{\text{Distance}}{\text{Time}}$ so, Distance OS = Speed x Time

= 0.9m/s x 1.283 x 3600s = 4,156.92m = 4.15692km = 4.157km (to 3dps)

(it is important during calculations to be aware of the units you are working in)

To calculate SR,

$Cos(26.6) = \dfrac{\text{Adjacent}}{\text{Hypotenuse}} = \dfrac{OS}{SR} = \dfrac{4.157}{SR} = 0.894$ So, $SR = \dfrac{4.157}{0.894} =$ **4.650 km**

(to obtain Cos(26.6) on the calculator, I press **cos** followed by **26.6** followed by **=**)

b) From S to R Speed = $\dfrac{\text{Distance}}{\text{Time}}$ so, Time = $\dfrac{\text{Distance}}{\text{Speed}} = \dfrac{4{,}650\text{m}}{0.9\text{m/s}} =$ 5,167s

5167s = $\dfrac{5167}{3600}$ hrs = 1.435 hrs (to 3dps)

The distance RO can be calculated using pythagoras's theorem:

$(SR)^2 = (OS)^2 + (OR)^2$ $(4.65)^2 = (4.157)^2 + (OR)^2$ $(OR)^2 = (4.65)^2 - (4.157)^2$

$(OR)^2 = 21.623 - 17.281 = 4.342$ So, OR = $\sqrt{4.342} = 2.084$ km

(The distance RO could also be calculated by:

$\text{Sin}(26.6) = \dfrac{OR}{4.65} = 0.448$ then, OR = 0.448 x 4.65 = 2.084 km)

Then, Speed = $\dfrac{\text{Distance}}{\text{Time}}$ & Time = $\dfrac{\text{Distance}}{\text{Speed}} = \dfrac{2{,}084}{0.9} = 2{,}315$s

$= \dfrac{2{,}315}{3{,}600}$ hrs = 0.643hr

Total time = 1.283 + 1.435 + 0.643 = **3.361hrs**

Forming and solving equations (Algebra)

Worked example:

A man decides to sell his old LPs and singles at a car boot sale for £4.50 and £2.50 respectively. He sells 34 records at the sale and his total takings are £113.00

a) Use this information to form two equations about the LPs and singles sold at the car boot sale.

Let the number of LPs sold = A and the number of singles sold = B

Then, **A + B = 34** (Equation 1)

and, **4.50A + 2.50B = 113.00** (Equation 2)

b) Use the equations to calculate the number of LPs and the number of singles sold at the car boot sale.

If A + B = 34 then A = 34 − B

We can now substitute A = 34 − B into equation 2:

So, 4.5(34 − B) + 2.5B = 113

Next, we expand the brackets:

4.5 x 34 − 4.5B + 2.5B = 113

$153 - 2B = 113$

$153 - 113 = 2B$

$40 = 2B$ therefore **B = 20**

We can now substitute B = 20 into equation 1

$A + 20 = 34$ therefore **A = 14**

So, the man sold **14** LPs and **20** singles

Practice Questions

Q1 In 2008, it was estimated that the UK's assets were worth approximately £337,104,120,000

a) Write down this figure in standard form.

b) If a painting is valued at twenty three and a half million pounds, what percentage of the UK's assets is the painting worth? (Give the answer in standard form to 4 decimal places.

Q2 If the diameter of an atom is in the order of 10^{-8} cm, then what would be the length of one hundred and fifty thousand atoms lying side by side (give the answer in standard form in metres).

Q3 A driver travels 63 miles from town A to town C, then travels at 42 miles per hour for 42 minutes from town C to town B. In town B the driver buys a new car.

a) If the new car emits 270g of carbon dioxide for every kilometre driven, then how many kilograms of carbon dioxide will the new car emit on its journey back to A? (1km = 0.621 miles).

b) Calculate the angle BAC. Check your answer by an alternative method.

Q4 A farmer is planning to use one of his fields for growing rapeseed and wishes to make a scale drawing of the field. If the area of the field is 1.8 Hectares, and the length of the field is twice its width, then:
a) What are the actual dimensions (in metres) of the field?
(1 Hectare = 10,000m²)

b) What will be the dimensions of the field on the scale drawing, if he chooses a scale of 1 : 200?

Q5 A travel company decides to sell its return flights to France and Germany on the internet. The flights to France are sold for £33.50 and the flights to Germany for £37.00. During the first week, the company sells 380 flights. The total takings for the flights are £13,629.50

a) Use this information to form two equations about the return flights to France and Germany sold on the internet.

b) Use the equations to calculate the number of return flights to France and Germany sold on the internet during the first week.

Answers to L1 Numeracy Learning Assessment

Part A

Q1 Busiest day – Friday (56)   Quietest day – Tuesday (33)   56
                                                              − 33
                                                               23

Q2 June (425)   January (250) $^3 4^1 2\,5$
                                   − 2 5 0
                                   1 7 5

Q3 **201,926**

Q4 **Twenty three thousand and sixty four**

Q5 **miles per hour**

Q6 jackal (35 miles per hour)   pig (10 miles per hour)   35
                                                            − 10
                                                            25 miles per hour

Q7 **A key (or legend)** is missing

Q8 **95kg**

Q9 **24°C**

Q10 **85,000**

Q11   38
     − 25
     13 minutes

Q12 8.25 + 25mins = 8.50 + 10mins = 9.00 + 10 mins = **9.10**

Part B

Q13

	Fraction	Percentage	Decimal
	1/2 (a half)	50%	0.5
	1/4 (a quarter)	25%	0.25
	3/4 (three quarters)	75%	0.75
	1/5 (a fifth)	20%	0.20
	2/5 (two fifths)	40%	0.40
	3/5 (three fifths)	60%	0.60
	4/5 (four fifths)	80%	0.80
	1/3 (a third)	33%	0.33

Q14 $\frac{1}{4}$ of 220 = $4 \overline{)22^{2}0}$ (quotient 055) **55** were women

Q15 $\frac{1}{3}$ of £180.00 = $3 \overline{)180.00}$ (quotient 060.00) $\frac{2}{3}$ = 60 x 2 = **£120**

Q16 Average = 132 ÷ 6 = $6 \overline{)13^{1}2}$ (quotient 022) = **22** minutes

Q17 Range = highest number – lowest number = 29 – 16 = **13** minutes

Q18 10% of £78̂2.00 = **£78.20**

Q19 10% of 7 0̂0. = 70   20% = 2 x 70 = **140**

Q20 10% of £1 1̂0.00 = £11.00   30% = 3 x £11.00 = £33.00
Therefore, cost of membership = £110.00 - £33.00 = **£77.00**

Q21 6 out of 30 = $\frac{6^{1}}{30_{5}}$ = $\frac{1}{5}$ = **20%**

Q22
£1.15		£1.80		£4.60	
x 4	+	£1.80	+	£3.60	
£4.60		£3.60		£8.20	Total = **£8.20**
2		1		1	

Q23
1.5
x 7
10.5 m²   Area = **10.5m²**
3

Q24 40 x 10 = 400   400 x 30 = 400 x 10 x 3 = 4,000 x 3 = **12,000 cm³**

Q25 £6.15 x 30 = £6.15 x 10 x 3 = £61.50 x 3 = £   61.50
                                            x ___3___
                                            £ 184.50 = **£184.50**
                                                  1

Q26 **11.1** seconds

Q27 **29m**

Q28 4 x 70g = **280g**

Q29 7 x 3 = **21km**

Q30 400g = 0.4kg   0.4kg x 40 = 0.4 x 10 x 4 = 4 x 4 = **16kg**

Answers to L1 Practice Questions

Q1a
$$\begin{array}{r} £8.65 \\ \times\quad 3 \\ \hline £25.95 \\ \scriptstyle 1\ \ 1 \end{array}$$
$= $ **£25.95**

Q1b
$£25.95 \div 3 = \dfrac{25.95}{3} = 3\overline{)25.\,^19^15}\ \overset{8\,.\,6\,5}{} = $ **£8.65**

Q1c
$$\begin{array}{r} {}^4\cancel{5}^9\cancel{0}.^9\cancel{0}^10 \\ -\ \ 2\,5\,.\,9\,5 \\ \hline 2\,4\,.\,0\,5 \end{array}$$
$= $ **£24.05**

Q2
$£44.61 \div 3 = \dfrac{44.61}{3} = 3\overline{)4\,^14.\,^26^21}\ \overset{1\,4.\,8\,7}{} = $ **£14.87**

Q3 A quarter of 36 = ¼ x 36 = $\dfrac{36}{4} = \dfrac{\cancel{36}^9}{\cancel{4}^1} = 9$ Therefore $\dfrac{3}{4}$ of 36 = 3 x 9 = **27**

Q4
$£85.00 \div 5 = \dfrac{85.00}{5} = 5\overline{)8\,^35.0\,0}\ \overset{1\,7.0\,0}{} = $ **£17.00**

Q5a
$$\begin{array}{r} 2.30 \\ 1.70 \\ 1.85 \\ 2.25 \\ 1.85 \\ 2.60 \\ +\ \ 2.15 \\ \hline 14.70 \\ \scriptstyle 3\ \ 2 \end{array}$$
$14.70 \div 7 = 7\overline{)14.70}\ \overset{2.1\,0}{} = $ **£2.10**

Q5b Range = highest number minus the lowest number
= £2.60 − £1.70 = **£0.90**

Q6a

One fifth of 820 = $\dfrac{1}{5}$ x 820   = $5\overline{)8^{3}2^{2}0}$ $\quad\overset{1\ 6\ 4}{}$

Therefore, two fifths of 820 = 2 x 164 = 164

$$\begin{array}{r} 164 \\ \times\ \ 2 \\ \hline \mathbf{328} \\ \hline \scriptstyle 1 \end{array}$$

Q6b

2/5 as a percentage = 40%
10% of 820 = 82
40% of 820 = 82 x 4   =   82

$$\begin{array}{r} 82 \\ \times\ \ 4 \\ \hline \mathbf{328} \\ \hline \end{array}$$

Q7

10% of 600 = 60
30% of 600 = 60

$$\begin{array}{r} 60 \\ \times\ \ 3 \\ \hline \mathbf{180} \\ \hline \end{array}$$

Q8a **60%**   b **0.6**

Q9a **0.1**   b **1/10**

Q10

108.9p x 30 = 108.9 x 10 x 3   =   1089

$$\begin{array}{r} 1089 \\ \times\ \ \ \ 3 \\ \hline 3267 \\ \hline \scriptstyle 2\ 2 \end{array} = 3267\text{p} = £\mathbf{32.67}$$

Q11

Area = length x width = 2.2 x 0.5 = 2.2 x ½ = 2.2 ÷ 2 = $2\overline{)2.2}$ $\overset{1.1}{}$ = **1.1**m²

Q12

Area = 42m² length = 7m width = ?
Area = length x width 42 = 7 x ?   So, ? = $\dfrac{42}{7}$ = 42 ÷ 7 = **6**m

Q13

Volume = length x width x height = 8m x 6m x 2.5m

$$\begin{array}{r} 2.5 \\ \times\ \ 8 \\ \hline 20.0 \\ \hline \scriptstyle 4 \end{array} \qquad \begin{array}{r} 20 \\ \times\ \ 6 \\ \hline 120 \\ \hline \end{array} = \mathbf{120}\text{m}^3$$

Q14

$$\begin{array}{r} 150 \\ \times\ \ 6 \\ \hline 900 \\ \hline \scriptstyle 3 \end{array} \qquad \begin{array}{r} 900 \\ \times\ \ 6 \\ \hline 5400 \\ \hline \end{array} = £\mathbf{5,400.00}$$

Q15 £6.20 x 20 = £6.20 x 10 x 2 = £62.00 x 2 = £124.00 per week

In 4 weeks, he will earn 124

$$\begin{array}{r} \times\ \ 3 \\ \hline 372 \end{array}\ =\ \textbf{£372.00}$$

1

Q16 14 out of 42 $=\ \dfrac{14}{42}\ =\ \dfrac{\overset{1}{\cancel{7}}}{\cancel{21}^{3}}\ =\ \dfrac{1}{3}\ =\ \textbf{33\%}$

Q17 3 out of 15 $=\ \dfrac{3}{15}\ =\ \dfrac{\overset{1}{\cancel{3}}}{\cancel{15}^{5}}\ =\ \dfrac{1}{5}\ =\ \textbf{20\%}$

Q18 Two hundredths of a second = 0.02 seconds

$$\begin{array}{r} 19.30 \\ +\ 0.02 \\ \hline 19.32 \end{array}\quad \text{previous world record}\ =\ \textbf{19.32}\ \text{seconds}$$

Q19
$$\begin{array}{r} 2^{1}0^{9\,1}.0 \\ -\ \ \ 3.4 \\ \hline 16.6 \end{array}\quad \text{The tailor has } \textbf{16.6}\text{m of cloth left}$$

Q20
$$\begin{array}{r} 5^{4}0^{9}.0^{9\,1}0 \\ -\ 22.3\ 8 \\ \hline 27.6\ 2 \end{array}\quad \text{He has £}\textbf{27.62}\ \text{left}$$

Q21
$$\begin{array}{r} 36^{5},0^{9\,1}00 \\ -23,350 \\ \hline 12,650 \end{array}\quad \text{They need £}\textbf{12,650}$$

Q22a
$$\begin{array}{r} 11.58 \\ -11.52 \\ \hline 0.06 \end{array}\ \text{million}\ =\ 60,000$$

So, there are **60,000** more pensioners than under-16s living in the UK

b 60,000 = **sixty thousand**

Q23 3 children : 1 carer

18 children : 6 carers

Q24 The car emits 300g of carbon dioxide per kilometre = 0.3kg/km

So, in 30km, it will emit 30 x 0.3 kg of carbon dioxide

0.3 x 30 = 0.3 x 10 x 3 = 3 x 3 = **9**kg

Q25 400g = 0.4kg
0.4 x 30 = 0.4 x 10 x 3 = 4 x 3 = **12**kg

Q26 1km = 1,000m   4km = 4,000m
0.5km = 500m 0.05km = 50m
Therefore, 4.05km = 4,000m + 50m = **4,050**m

Q27 100cm = 1m   50cm = 0.5m = ½ m
So, how many 0.5m are there in a 7.5m roll? **15**

Q28 1km = 1,000m   3.5km = 3,500m
So, how many 50m lengths are there in 3,500m?

0 0 7 0   =   70 lengths
3,500 ÷ 50   =   50)3,500

Q29 **65**kg

Q30 **50.3**m

Answers to L2 Numeracy Learning Guide

Forming and Simplifying Fractions

Q1 Total number of visitors = 43 + 28 +33 +36 = 140
The proportion of visitors who played table tennis = 28 out of 140 = $\frac{28}{140}$

$$\frac{28}{140} = \frac{14}{70} = \frac{7}{35} = \frac{1}{5}$$

Q2 Total number of children = 41 + 17 + 20 + 41 +34 = 153
The proportion of children who chose indoor sports = 17 out of 153 = $\frac{17}{153}$

$$\frac{17}{153} = \frac{1}{9}$$

Calculating Percentages - Conversion Table

	Fraction	Percentage	Decimal
	1/8 (an eighth)	12.5%	0.125
	1/4 (a quarter)	25%	0.25
	3/8 (three eighths)	37.5%	0.375
	5/8 (five eighths)	62.5%	0.625

	Fraction	Percentage	Decimal
	7/8 (seven eighths)	87.5%	0.875
	1/6 (one sixth)	16.7%	0.167
	1/7 (one seventh)	14.3%	0.143
	2/7 (two sevenths)	28.6%	0.286
	3/7 (three sevenths)	42.9%	0.429
	4/7 (four sevenths)	57.1%	0.571
	1/9 (one ninth)	11.1%	0.111
	2/9 (two ninths)	22.2%	0.222
	4/9 (four ninths)	44.4%	0.444

	Fraction	Percentage	Decimal
	1/10 (one tenth)	10%	0.1
	3/10 (three tenths)	30%	0.3

Calculating Percentages

Q1 57% of the people are men, therefore 43% of the people are women.
To find 43% of 900
10% of 900 = 90   40% of 900 = 90 x 4 = 360
1% of 900 = 9   3% of 900 = 9 x 3 = 27
Therefore 43% of 900 = 360 + 27 = **387**

Q2 To find 17.5% of £16,500.00
10% of £16,500.00 = £1,650.00
1% of £16,500.00 = £165.00   7% of £16,500 = 165

$$\begin{array}{r} 165 \\ \times\quad 7 \\ \hline 1,155 \\ \hline \end{array} = £1,155$$

0.5% of £16,500.00 = 165.00 ÷ 2

$$165.00 \div 2 = 2\overline{)165.^{1}00}\quad \frac{82.50}{}$$

17.5% = 10% + 7% + 0.5%   =   1,650.00
                                                1,155.00
                                         +   82.50
                                         ─────────────
                                             2,887.50   =   £2,887.50

Therefore, the cost of the car =   16,500.00
                                         + 2,887.50
                                         ─────────────
                                             19,387.50   = **£19,387.50**

Q3 To find 26% of 23,600

10% of 23,600 = 2,360   1%   =   236

20%   =   2,360   6%   =   236
          x   2   x   6
         4,720   1,416
           1   2 3

So, 26% = 20% + 6%   =   4,720
                        +1,416
                        6,136
                          1

Q4 16% of 350 chose Turkish as their preferred cuisine

10% of 350 = 35   1% of 350 = 3.5   6% of 350 = 3.5
                                             x   6
                                             21.0
                                               3

Total number = 35 + 21 = **56**

Calculating percentage increase (or decrease)

Q1a Percentage increase in the house price of House 1 =

$$\frac{\text{actual increase}}{\text{original amount}} \times 100\%$$

$$= \frac{24,000}{120,000} \times 100\% = \frac{24}{120} \times 100\% = \frac{2}{10} \times 100\% = \frac{1}{5} \times 100\% = \mathbf{20\%}$$

Q1b Percentage decrease in the house price of House 2 =

$$\frac{\text{actual decrease}}{\text{original amount}} \times 100\%$$

$$= \frac{12,000}{120,000} \times 100\% = \frac{12}{120} \times 100\% = \frac{1}{10} \times 100\% = \mathbf{10\%}$$

Q2 Percentage increase in the party's vote $= \dfrac{\text{actual increase}}{\text{original amount}} \times 100\%$

actual increase = $16^{5,1}250$ original amount = 12,500
                 $-12,500$
                 $\overline{\ \ 3,750\ }$

Percentage increase =

$$\frac{3,750}{12,500} \times 100\% = \frac{3750\ (\div 5)}{125\ (\div 5)} = \frac{750\ (\div 5)}{25\ (\div 5)} = \frac{150}{5} = \textbf{30}\%$$

Q3 Percentage increase in temperature $= \dfrac{\text{actual increase}}{\text{original amount}} \times 100\%$

actual increase = 37.8°C - 36°C = 1.8°C   original amount = 36 °C

$$\text{Percentage increase} = \frac{1.8 \times 100\%}{36} = \frac{180\ (\div 9)}{36\ (\div 9)} = \frac{20}{4} = \textbf{5\%}$$

Calculations involving Multiplication

Q1 £5.85 x 36 hours
    (36 = 30 + 6)

£5.85 x 30	=	£58.50
	x	3
		£175.50
		2 1

£5.85 x 6	=	£5.85
	x	6
		£35.10
		5 3

So, £5.85 x 36 = 175.50
                + 35.10
                £210.60
                  1 1

Q2 8 hours overtime at time and a half = 8 + 4 = 12 hours

    £5.85 x 12 = £5.85
                x   12
                £70.20
                 10   6

Q3a £6.00 x 42.5 hours
     (42.5 = 40 + 2 + 0.5)

£6.00 x 40 = £60.00   £6.00 x 2 = £12.00   £6.00 x 0.5 = £3.00

x   4
£240.00

So, £6.00 x 40 = 240.00
12.00
+   3.00
£255.00   per week

Q3b

255
x   4
£1,020   in 4 weeks
2 2

Q4a

£6.30 x 175 hours
£6.30 x 175
(175 = 100 + 70 + 5)

£6.30 x 100 = £630.00   £6.30 x 70 = £63.00   £6.30
x   7   x   5
£441.00   £31.50
2   1

So, £6.30 x 175   =   630.00
441.00
+   31.50
£1,102.50
1

Q4b

1,102.50
x   12
£13,230.00
1   3 6

Q5

Area of lawn A = length x width = 16m x 11m   =   16
x 11
176m²
6

Area of lawn B = length x width = 13m x 7m   =   13
x 7
91m²
2

$$\text{Combined area of A and B} = \begin{array}{r} 176 \\ +\ \ 91 \\ \hline \mathbf{267}\text{m}^2 \\ \hline {\scriptstyle 1} \end{array}$$

Q6 Area of warehouse = length x width = 63m x 22.4m

(63 = 60 + 3)

$$22.4 \times 60 = \begin{array}{r} 224 \\ \times\ \ \ 6 \\ \hline 1{,}344\text{m}^2 \\ {\scriptstyle 1\ 2} \end{array} \qquad 22.4 \times 3 = \begin{array}{r} 22.4 \\ \times\ \ \ 3 \\ \hline 67.2\text{m}^2 \\ {\scriptstyle 1} \end{array}$$

$$\text{Therefore, area} = \begin{array}{r} 1{,}344.0 \\ +\ \ \ \ \ 67.2 \\ \hline \mathbf{1{,}411.2}\ \text{m}^2 \\ {\scriptstyle 1\ 1} \end{array}$$

Q7 Volume of topsoil = length x width x height
Length = 22m   Width = 15m   Height (or Depth) = 20cm = 0.2m = 1/5m
Volume = 22 x 15 x 1/5

$$\underset{5}{15} \times 1/5 = \frac{15}{5} = 3 \qquad 22 \times 3 = \mathbf{66}\text{m}^3$$

Q8 450g x 33
450g = 0.45kg
(33 = 30 + 3)

$$0.45\text{kg} \times 30 = \begin{array}{r} 4.5 \\ \times\ \ \ 3 \\ \hline 13.5\text{kg} \\ {\scriptstyle 1} \end{array} \qquad 0.45 \times 3 = \begin{array}{r} 0.45 \\ \times\ \ \ 3 \\ \hline 1.35\text{kg} \\ {\scriptstyle 1\ 1} \end{array}$$

$$\text{Weight of soup} = \begin{array}{r} 13.50 \\ +\ \ 1.35 \\ \hline \mathbf{14.85}\ \text{kg} \\ \hline \end{array}$$

Mean, Range, Median and Mode

Q1a Average cost of the flights $= \dfrac{\text{Total cost}}{\text{Number of flights}}$

Total cost $=$ Number of flights $= 13$

$$
\begin{array}{r}
43 \\
47 \\
43 \\
47 \\
43 \\
47 \\
43 \\
53 \\
46 \\
56 \\
46 \\
61 \\
+\ 49 \\
\hline
624 \\
\end{array}
$$

$^6\ \ 4\ \ 8.\,0\,0 = £\textbf{48.00}$

Therefore, average cost $= £624.00 \div 13 = 13\overline{)62^{10}4.00}$

Q1b Range of flight costs over the week =
highest cost − lowest cost = £61.00 - £43.00 = £**18.00**

Q1c Median cost =
43 + 43 + 43 + 43 + 46 + 46 + **47** + 47 + 47 + 49 + 53 + 56 + 61
= £**47.00**

Q1d The mode = £**43.00**
(i.e. the number which occurs most frequently).

Ratios

Q1 Ratio of hospitality : retail : sport : leisure : engineering =
36 : 18 : 24 : 12 (÷ 6) = **6 : 3 : 4 : 2**

Q2 Ratio of apprenticeship trainees across the 4 NVQs =
Food and drink service : Food processing : Customer service :
Front of house
15 : 9 : 6 : 6 (÷ 3) = **5 : 3 : 2 : 2**

Q3 Ratio of 'boxes of strawberries' to 'boxes of blueberries' sold in one day

  13 : 2
208 : ?

208 is 16 times 13 so number of boxes of blueberries = 16 x 2 = **32**

Q4a Ratio of ascents on highest mountain to ascents on second highest
mountain

= 145 : 45 (÷5) = **29 : 9**

Q4b Ratio of ascents on 2nd highest mountain to ascents on 5th highest
mountain

= 45 : 45 = **1 : 1**

Answers to Level 2 Functional Skills Numeracy

1a

$40g \times 18 = 180$

$$\begin{array}{r} \times \ 4 \\ \hline 720g \\ \scriptstyle 3 \end{array} = \textbf{0.72kg}$$

b

18×200 calories $= 3,600$ calories

240 calories $= 1$ kilojoule

Therefore, $3,600$ calories $= \dfrac{3,60\cancel{0}}{24\cancel{0}} = \dfrac{\cancel{360}^{30}}{\cancel{24}^{2}} = \textbf{15 kilojoules}$

c

$$\dfrac{9.2g}{40} \times 100\% = \dfrac{92\cancel{0}}{4\cancel{0}} = 4\overline{)9^{1}2}\,^{23} = \textbf{23\%}$$

d

$6\% = 0.3g$ Therefore, $1\% = \dfrac{0.3g}{6} = 6\overline{)0.30}\,^{0.05g}$

$1\% = 0.05g$ Therefore, $100\% = \textbf{5g}$

e

$$\dfrac{0.5g}{40g} \times 100\% = \dfrac{5\cancel{0}}{4\cancel{0}} = \textbf{1.25\%} < 2\%$$

Therefore, the claim is true.

f

12 : 8 : 2 : 3 : 4 : 4

60g : ? : 10g : ? : 20g : 20g

The 2 parts of parmesan weigh 10g   Therefore, 1 part would weigh 5g

There are 8 parts gorgonzola and 3 parts walnuts

The weight of the of gorgonzola = 8 x 5g = **40g**

The weight of the walnuts = 3 x 5g = **15g**

g

7% = 133 calories   Therefore, 1% = $\frac{133}{7}$ calories = $7\overline{)13^63}$ 1 9 calories

1% = 19 calories   100% = **1,900 calories**

h

6% = 114 calories   Therefore, 1% = 114 calories = $6\overline{)11^54}$ calories 1 9

1% = 19 calories   100% = **1,900 calories**

Therefore, the guidelines are the same.

2a

$33,\overset{3}{4}\overset{1}{3}4$
$-33,092$
342 kWh

b

342 x 5.296

300 x 5.296 = 529.6
         x   3
      1,588.8
         2 1

40 x 5.296 = 52.96
       x   4
     211.84
     1 3 2

$$2 \times 5.296 = \begin{array}{r} 5.296 \\ \times \quad 2 \\ \hline 10.592 \\ 11 \end{array}$$

$$\begin{array}{r} 1588.8 \\ 211.84 \\ + \quad 10.592 \\ \hline 1811.232p \\ 1121 \end{array} = \textbf{£18.11} \text{ (to the nearest penny)}$$

c

$$\begin{array}{r} 1\,{}^7\!8\,{}^9\!0\,{}^1\!2\,4 \\ -1\,7\,\underline{5\,3\,1} \\ \textbf{4\,9\,3} \textbf{ kWh} \end{array}$$

d

$$493 \times 12.472 \qquad 400 \times 12.472 = \begin{array}{r} 1247.2 \\ \times \quad 4 \\ \hline 4988.8 \\ 12 \end{array}$$

$$90 \times 12.472 = \begin{array}{r} 124.72 \\ \times \quad 9 \\ \hline 1122.48 \\ 2461 \end{array}$$

$$3 \times 12.472 = \begin{array}{r} 12.472 \\ \times \quad 3 \\ \hline 37.416 \\ 12 \end{array}$$

$$\begin{array}{r} 4988.8 \\ 1122.48 \\ + \quad 37.416 \\ \hline 6148.696p \\ 1111 \end{array} = \textbf{£61.47} \text{ (to the nearest penny)}$$

e

$$\begin{array}{r} £18.11 \\ + \quad £61.47 \\ \hline \textbf{£79.58} \end{array}$$

f

$$\frac{£79.58}{40} = \frac{7.958}{4} = 4\overline{)7.^39^35^38}^{\;\;1.9\,8\,9\;r2} = \textbf{£1.99} \text{ (to the nearest penny)}$$

g

24% of £537.60

10% = £53.76   20% = 53.76
                        + 53.76
                          £107.52
                           ‾‾‾‾
                           1 1

1% = 5.376   4% = 5.376
                        x   4
                        £21.504
                         ‾‾‾‾‾
                         1 3 2

Therefore, 24% = 107.52
                +   21.50
                  £129.02
                  ‾‾‾‾‾‾‾

h

37% - 27% = 10%

10% of £537.60 = **£53.76**

i

10% of £537.60 = £53.76

$$5\% \text{ of } £537.60 = \frac{£53.76}{2} = 2\overline{)5^13.^17^16}^{\;\;2\,6.\,8\,8}$$

Therefore, 15% of £537.60 = 53.76
                          + 26.88
                            80.64
                            ‾‾‾‾‾
                            11 1

However £80.64 < £85.00 so the student would not make a saving.

j

$$\frac{6.5}{34} = \frac{65^{13}}{340^{68}} = \frac{13}{68} \approx \frac{1}{5}$$

K

6.5 kg per 1,000 hours

Number of hours per leap year = 366 x 24 = 366 x 12 x 2

```
    366          4,392
x    12       +  4,392
  4,392          8,784  hours
    77              1
```

For every 1,000 hours, 6.5kg of Carbon Dioxide is produced

Therefore, for 8,784 hours, 8.784 x 6.5kg of Carbon Dioxide is produced

```
                                 4.392
    8.784    8.784 x ½  =    2)8.7¹84
x       6
  52.704                       52.704
    4 5 2                   +   4.392
                             57.096 kg
                                 1
```

3a

Student A's car: $\frac{420 \text{ miles}}{40 \text{ litres}}$ = $\begin{array}{r} 10.5 \text{ miles/litre} \\ 4)\overline{42.0} \end{array}$

Student B's car: 16km/litre = 10 miles/litre

Therefore, **Student A** has the more fuel efficient car

b

12½ % of 40L

10% = 4L   1% = 0.4L   2% = 0.8L   0.5% = 0.2L

Therefore, 12½ % of 40L = 4 + 0.8 + 02 = 5L

Student B's car therefore takes 45L

4.5L ≈ 1 gallon, so 45L ≈ **10 gallons**

c

$$1\text{cm} : 2{,}000{,}000 \text{ cm} = 1\text{cm} : 20{,}000 \text{ m} = 1\text{cm} : 20 \text{ km}$$
$$33\text{cm} : \ ?$$

Estimated distance = 20 km x 33 = 660 km

1 mile ≈ 1.6 km $\dfrac{1}{1.6}$ mile = 1 km

Therefore, 660 km = $\dfrac{660}{1.6}$ miles = $\dfrac{66^{33}00}{16^{8}}$ = $8\overline{)33^{1}0^{2}0^{4}0}$ = 4 1 2.5 miles

Therefore, the difference between the estimation (412.5 miles) and the Sat-Nav reading (420 miles) is **7.5 miles**

d

The distance to Edinburgh and back is 840 miles
Student A's car does 10.5 miles/litre

So, the amount of fuel used = $\dfrac{840}{10.5}$ = $\dfrac{8400}{105}$ = $105\overline{)8400}$ = 80 Litres

If the cost of the fuel is shared equally, each student will pay for 20 litres

20L x 133.9p/litre = £13.39
$$\begin{array}{r} \text{x} \quad 2 \\ \hline 26.78 \\ \hline \tiny 1 \end{array}$$

Therefore, each student should pay **£26.80** (to the nearest ten pence)

e

Highest temperature: London, 20°C
Lowest temperature: Edinburgh, 8 °C
Therefore, temperature range across the five capital cities = **12°C**

f

1.4mm
0.7mm
0.1mm
0.9mm
0.0mm
3.1mm
2

Average rainfall $= 3.1 \div 5 = 5\overline{)3.1^{1}0}$ $\dfrac{0.6\,2}{}$ $= $ **0.62mm**

g

Aberdeen, with a temperature range of 10°C

h

Leuchars

i

16 hours and 12 minutes

j

$\dfrac{97\cancel{0,000}}{1,\cancel{000,000}} \times 1\cancel{00}\% = $ **97%**

K

```
  1,900,000
- 1,200,000
    700,000   x 5 = 3,500,000
```

3,500,000 x £75 = 245,000,000
+ 17,500,000
= £**262,500,000**
1

4

Product	Supermarket	
	Safeburies	**Morose**
1 Litre of skimmed milk	£0.83	£0.86
2 x 1 litre cartons of orange juice	£1.75 per carton **£2.50**	£1.95 per carton **£1.95**
Broccoli (335g)	£1.27	£1.35
Organic spinach	£1.00	£1.10
Large wholemeal loaf of Bread (800g)	£1.36	£1.38
600g bag of apples	£1.67	£1.70
2 kg of bananas	35p/lb **£1.54**	35p/lb **£1.54**
1 kg of carrots	30p/lb **£0.66**	35p/lb **£0.77**
Peppered steak (435g)	£4.00	£4.00 **)**
Pork loin steaks (0.66kg)	£4.00	£4.00 **) £10.00**
Chicken (1.45kg)	£4.00	£4.00 **)**
Original coffee granules (200g)	£4.00	£3.85
Pure vegetable oil (1L)	£1.10	£1.25
Salted butter (750g)	£0.98	£0.94
12 free range medium eggs	£2.73	£2.80
Milk chocolate digestives	£1.00	£1.10
Easy cook rice	£1.06	£1.06
3 in 1 Shampoo	£2.20	£2.45
TOTAL	**£35.90**	**£34.10**

a

Student A's car does 10.5 miles/litre

Therefore, 16 miles (10½ + 5½) requires approximately 1½ litres

At 133.9p/litre, cost of petrol used to drive to Morose ≈ £1.34 + £0.67 = £2.01

Therefore, cost of shopping trip to Morose = £34.10 + £2.01 = £36.11

Therefore, it would be more economical for Student A to shop at Safeburies, since:

£35.90 < £36.11

b

The statement should read '10 items or fewer', since the items are countable. For example, there was less crime in the town centre last year (you can't count crime); there were fewer crimes committed in the town centre last year (you can count the number of crimes).

c

10% of £35.90 = £3.59   40% = 3.59

$$\begin{array}{r} 3.59 \\ \times \quad 4 \\ \hline 14.36 \\ \scriptstyle 2\ 3 \end{array}$$

d

Safeburies: 10% of £35.90 = £3.59   Therefore, on-line cost = $3\,5.^{8}\overset{1}{9}0$

$$\begin{array}{r} 3\,5.^{8}\overset{1}{9}0 \\ - \quad 3.59 \\ \hline £\,32.31 \end{array}$$

Morose: 5% of £34.10 = £3.40 ÷ 2 = £1.70

Therefore, on-line cost = $3^{3}4.^{1}10$

$$\begin{array}{r} 3^{3}4.^{1}10 \\ - \quad 1.70 \\ \hline £\,32.40 \end{array}$$

Therefore, **Safeburies** would be cheaper on-line for Student A's shopping (by 9p).

e

Model A does not have unlimited texts

Model D: 1st year cost = £20 x 12 = £240
         2nd year cost = £10 x 12 = £120

Total cost = £360 which is above student A's maximum price.

Model C: cost over 2 years =
         (£15 x 24) - £50 = £360 - £50 = £310 < £350

Model B: Cost over 2 years = £15 x 21 = £315 < £350

Model C has more memory and minutes than Model B, so Student A should choose **Model C**

5a

Total number of students = 19

Total number of students who have competed all the requirements
of the Functional Skills L2 English = 13

Therefore, fraction of students who have competed = $\dfrac{\mathbf{13}}{\mathbf{19}}$

b

For group 1, 5 out of 8 passed =

$$\frac{5}{8} \times 100\% = \frac{500}{8} = \frac{250}{4} = \frac{125}{2} = 62.5\%$$

For group 2, 7 out of 11 passed =

$$\frac{7}{11} \times 100\% = \frac{700}{11} = 11\overline{)70^40.^70^40} \qquad 63.63 \; r7 = 63.6\%$$

Therefore, the difference between the percentage pass rates = 63.6
-    62.5
1.1%

c

Total number of students = 19

Number of students who passed L2 maths = 12

Therefore, the overall percentage pass rate in maths = $\dfrac{12}{19} \times 100\% = \dfrac{1200}{19}$

$$= 19\overline{)120^60.^30^{11}0} \qquad 63.15 \; r15 = \mathbf{63.2\%}$$

d

The new overall percentage pass rate = $\dfrac{14}{19} \times 100\% = \dfrac{1400}{19}$

$$= 19\overline{)140^70.^{13}0^{16}0} \qquad 73.68 \; r8 = \mathbf{73.7\%}$$

UK Unemployment

		Short-term (Less than a year)	Long-term (More than a year)
18 – 24 years	Male	299,000	135,000
	Female	226,000	85,000
25 – 49 years	M	332,000	281,000
	F	328,000	155,000
50+ years	M	136,000	134,000
	F	79,000	50,000
Total	M	767,000	550,000
	F	633,000	290,000
		1,400,000	**840,000**

f

Total number of short-term unemployed people = 1,400,000

Total number of long-term unemployed people = 840,000

Ratio of short-term unemployed to long-term unemployed =

1,40~~0,000~~ : 84~~0,000~~ = 140 : 84 = 70 : 42 = 35 : 21 = **5 : 3**

g

Number of short-term unemployed people (50+) = 136,000

+ 79,000

215,000

Number of long-term unemployed people (50+) = 134,000

+ 50,000

184,000

Therefore, there are 215,000 – 184,000 = **31,000 more short-term unemployed adults.**

h

In the 18 – 24 years old age range, how many more male unemployed adults are there than female unemployed adults?

Number of male unemployed adults (18 - 24) = 299,000

+ 135,000

434,000

Number of male unemployed adults (18 - 24) = 226,000
                                            + 85,000
                                            ‾‾‾‾‾‾‾‾
                                               311,000
                                               ‾‾‾
                                               1 1

Therefore, there are 434,000 − 311,000 = **123,000 more male unemployed adults.**

i

0.5 million = **Five hundred thousand**

6

	Mon	Tues	Weds	Thurs	Fri	Sat	Sun	Total
9 – 10	1	0	4	3	1	5		**14**
10 – 11	4	5	7	5	3	5	3	**32**
11 – 12	4	6	7	8	5	4	4	**38**
12 – 1	6	9	10	6	3	7	4	**45**
1 – 2	5	8	9	9	8	9	8	**56**
2 – 3	7	6	10	10	8	9	6	**56**
3 - 4	8	3	8	9	8	6	4	**46**
4 - 5	4	5	5	4	4	5		**27**
5 - 6	6	5	9	8	7	6		**41**
6 - 7				6	5	2		**13**
7 - 8				4	3	3		**10**
Total	**45**	**47**	**69**	**72**	**55**	**61**	**29**	**378**

a

$\dfrac{45}{9}$ = **5 books per hour**

b

$$\dfrac{378}{7} = 7)\overline{37^28}^{\,54}$$

c

$\dfrac{56}{7}$ = **8**

d

$10 - 0 = $ **10**

e

29 (Sun), 45 (Mon), 47 (Tues), 55 (Fri), 61 (Sat), 69 (Wed), 72 (Thurs)
The median occurred on **Friday** (55)

f

$\dfrac{55}{11} = $ **5**

g

Percentage increase $= \dfrac{\text{actual increase}}{\text{original amount}} \times 100\% = \dfrac{(420 - 378)}{378} \times 100\%$

$= \dfrac{^{14}\cancel{42}}{^{126}\cancel{378}} \times 100\% = \dfrac{7}{63} \times 100\% =$

$\dfrac{1}{9} \times 100\% = \dfrac{100}{9} = 9\overline{)10^10.^10} \quad \begin{array}{r} 1\,1.\,1\text{'} \end{array} = $ **11.1%** (to 1dp)

h

140 cm	125 cm	160 cm
$\updownarrow 4$	$\updownarrow 5$	$\updownarrow 8$
35cm	25cm	20cm

Number of boxes that can fit in the space $= 4 \times 5 \times 8 = 160$

There are 6 books per box, so maximum number of books $= \begin{array}{r} 160 \\ \times \quad 6 \\ \hline \mathbf{960}\ \textbf{books} \\ {\scriptstyle 3} \end{array}$

i

$\dfrac{72}{378} \times 360° = \dfrac{24}{126} \times 360 = \dfrac{12}{^{21}\cancel{63}} \times {}^{120}\cancel{360} = \dfrac{4}{7} \times 120 = \dfrac{480}{7} = 7\overline{)4\,8^60.^40} \quad \begin{array}{r} 6\,8.5 \end{array}$

$= $ **69°** (to the nearest whole number).

j

$$\frac{45}{378} \times 100\% = \frac{15}{126} \times 100\% = \frac{5}{42} \times 100\% = \frac{500}{42} = \frac{250}{21} = 21\overline{)2\,5^4 0.^{19} 0}^{\ 1\,1.\ 9\,r1}$$

= **12%** (to the nearest whole number)

k

Bar chart showing book sales

l

Line graph comparing hourly book sales on Thursday and Friday

7

Site A, cost/m² $= \dfrac{£420}{48} = \dfrac{210}{24} = \dfrac{105}{12} = \dfrac{35}{4} = 4\overline{)35.^30^20}$ $\dfrac{8.75}{\ } = £8.75/m^2$

Site B, cost/m² $= \dfrac{£360}{42} = \dfrac{180}{21} = \dfrac{60}{7} = 7\overline{)60.^40^50^10}$ $8.571\ r3 = £8.57/m^2$

Site C, cost/m² $= \dfrac{£468}{54} = \dfrac{234}{27} = \dfrac{78}{9} = \dfrac{26}{3} = 3\overline{)26.^20^20^20}$ $8.666' = £8.67/m^2$

Therefore, **Site B @ £8.57/ m²** offers the best value for money.

6 people per day use the facilities and pay £20 each.

6 x £20 = £120 per day = £600 per week

Annual rent = £360
$$\begin{array}{r} \times \quad 12 \\ \hline £4{,}320 \\ \hline \scriptstyle 7 \end{array}$$

£600 x 7 = £4,200   £600 x 8 = £4,800

Therefore, 8 weeks are required for the woman to cover the cost of the annual rent.

b

Area = length x width
So, b = 42m² = 7m x **6m**

c

Scale = 1 : 25
         c : 7m

Therefore, c $= \dfrac{7}{25}$ m $= \dfrac{700}{25}$ cm = **28 cm**

d

$$d = \frac{6}{25}\,m = \frac{600}{25}\,cm = \textbf{24 cm}$$

e

Scale $= 1 : 25$

      $11\ cm : e$

Therefore, $e = 11cm \times 25 = 275\ cm = \textbf{2.75m}$

f

$$f = 9cm \times 25 = 225cm = \textbf{2.25m}$$

g

Desk area $= 4m \times 1.5m = \textbf{6m}^2$

h

$$h = \frac{4}{25}\,m = \frac{400}{25}\,cm = \textbf{16 cm}$$

i

$$i = \frac{1.5}{25}\,m = \frac{150}{25}\,cm = \textbf{6 cm}$$

j

$$j = 7cm \times 25 = 175cm = \textbf{1.75m}$$

k

$$k = 5cm \times 25 = 125cm = \textbf{1.25m}$$

l

Area $(7m^2) = 2 \times l$

Therefore, $l = \textbf{3.5m}$

m

$$m = \frac{3.5}{25} \text{ m} = \frac{350}{25} \text{ cm} = \textbf{14 cm}$$

n

$$n = \frac{2}{25} \text{ m} = \frac{200}{25} \text{ cm} = \textbf{8 cm}$$

8a

32% of 19,200,000

10% = 1,920,000   30% = 1,920,000
$$\times \quad \underline{\quad\quad 3}$$
$$\underline{5,760,000}$$
$$_2$$

1% = 192,000   2% = 192,000
$$\times \quad \underline{\quad\quad 2}$$
$$\underline{384,000}$$
$$_1$$

Therefore, 32% = 5,760,000
+ $\underline{\quad 384,000}$
                $\underline{6,144,000}$ = **6,100,000**
                $_{1\ \ 1}$

(to the nearest one hundred thousand).

b

68% of 19,200,000

60% = 1,920,000
$$\times \quad \underline{\quad\quad 6}$$
$$\underline{11,520,000}$$
$$_{5\ 1}$$

8% = 192,000
$$\times \quad \underline{\quad\quad 8}$$
$$\underline{1,536,000}$$
$$_{7\ 1}$$

Therefore, 68% = 11,520,000

+ <u> 1,536,000</u>

<u>13,056,000</u> = **13,100,000**

(to the nearest one hundred thousand)

c

19,200,000 = 42%

$$\frac{19,200,000}{42} \times 100\% = \frac{9,6\overset{32}{}00,000}{2\cancel{1}^{7}} \times 100\% = \frac{3,200,000}{7} \times 100\%$$

$$= \frac{320,000,000}{7} = 7\overline{)3\,2^{4}0,^{5}0^{1}0^{3}0,^{2}0^{6}0^{4}0.^{5}0}\quad \overset{4\,5,7\,1\,4,2\,8\,5.}{}$$

= **45,700,000** (to the nearest one hundred thousand).

d

Percentage increase = $\dfrac{\text{actual increase}}{\text{original amount}} \times 100\%$

$$= \frac{11m}{60m} \times 100\% = \frac{1,10\theta}{60} = \frac{55}{3} = 3\overline{)5^{2}5.^{1}0^{1}0}\quad \overset{1\,8.3\,3'}{}$$

= **18.3 million** (to on decimal place).

e

$6^{0}\cancel{+},^{10}\cancel{+}^{1}1\,3,^{1}\cancel{2}^{9}\cancel{0}^{1}5$

$-\,6\,0,\,4\,3\,2,0\,9\,8$

<u>   **6 8 1,1 0 7**</u>

f

10% of 30 million = 3,000,000 people

100,000 people per month x 12 = 1,200,000 people in one year

= 2,400,000 people in two years

= 3,600,000 people in three years

Therefore, it would take two and a half years for the number of Facebook accounts to reduce by 10% which would take us to **the end of October, 2013.**

g

$$45,000,\cancel{000} : 5,\cancel{000} = \cancel{45}^9,000 : 5^1 = \textbf{9,000 : 1}$$

h

10% of 50,760,000 = 5,076,000

$$\begin{array}{r} 80\% = 5,076,000 \\ \times 8 \\ \hline 40,608,000 \\ {}_{6\,4} \end{array}$$

1% = 507,600

$$\begin{array}{r} 9\% = 507,600 \\ \times 9 \\ \hline 4,568,400 \\ {}_{6\,5} \end{array}$$

$$\begin{array}{r} \text{Therefore, } 89\% = 40,608,000 \\ + 4,568,400 \\ \hline 45,176,400 \\ {}_{11} \end{array}$$

Therefore, non BME population of England ≈ **45,200,000**

i

$$\frac{10,000}{80,000} \times 100\% = \frac{1}{8} \times 100\% = \textbf{12.5\% > 11\%}$$

Therefore, Bedford has a higher than average BME population within England.

j

We need to calculate 14.3% of 382,000

10% = 38,200

1% = 3,820

$$\begin{array}{r} 4\% = 3,820 \\ \times 4 \\ \hline 15,280 \\ {}_{3} \end{array}$$

0.1% = 382   0.3% = 382
                          x   3
                          1,146
                           2

Therefore, 14.3% = 38,200
                   15,280
                +   1,146
                   54,626
                    1   1

k

Comparison of work-related incidents of ill health and injury – 2009/10

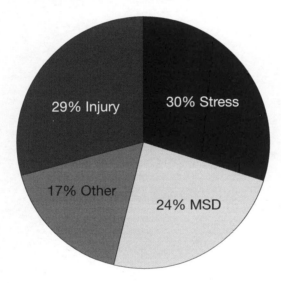

Comparison of days lost due to work-related ill health and injury – 2009/10

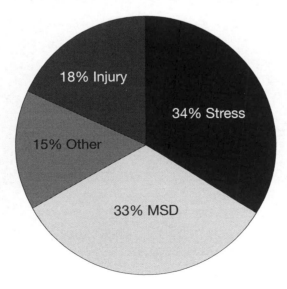

m

Actual decrease = 1,500 – 1,350 = 150

Percentage decrease = $\dfrac{\text{actual decrease}}{\text{original amount}}$ x 100% = $\dfrac{150}{1,500}$ x 1̶0̶0̶% = **10%**

9a

26/11/2010

b

862 x £0.40

800 x 0.4 = 40 x 8 = 320

60 x 0.4 = 4 x 6 = 24

2 x 0.4 = 0.8

Therefore, employee's travel allowance = **£344.80**

C

6.4% of £2,345.00

1% = £23.45   6% = 23.45
                  x   6
                  ‾‾‾‾‾‾‾‾
                    140.70
                    2 2 3

0.1% = £2.35   (to the nearest penny)   0.4% = 2.35
                                          x   4
                                          ‾‾‾‾‾‾‾
                                            9.40
                                            1 2

Therefore, employee's pension contribution = 140.70
                                          +   9.40
                                          ‾‾‾‾‾‾‾‾
                                           £150.10
                                             1 1

d

Gross pay = Salary + Project Allowance + Travel Expenses

$$
\begin{array}{r}
2,345.00 \\
90.00 \\
+\quad 344.80 \\
\hline
\mathbf{£2,779.80} \\
\end{array}
$$
1

e

$$
\begin{array}{r}
349.00 \\
183.27 \\
+\ 150.10 \\
\hline
\mathbf{£682.37} \\
\end{array}
$$
1 1

f

$$
\begin{array}{r}
£\,2,\!{}^6\!7\!{}^1\!7\,9.{}^7\!8\,{}^1\!0 \\
-\ £\quad 6\,8\,2.3\,7 \\
\hline
£\ \ \mathbf{2,0\,9\,7.4\,3} \\
\end{array}
$$

g

$$
\begin{array}{r}
£\ \ 2,\!345 \\
\times\qquad 12 \\
\hline
\mathbf{£28,\!140} \\
\end{array}
$$
4   5 6

10a

The student's BMI falls within the '**Obese**' category i.e. with a value > 30
(where the horizontal line at 1.7m crosses the vertical line at 90kg

b

$$
\text{Body Mass Index} = \frac{90}{(1.7)^2} = \frac{90}{1.7 \times 1.7} = \frac{90}{2.89} = \frac{9{,}000}{289} = 289\overline{)9{,}00\,0^{33}0.^{41}0}\ ^{3\ 1.\ 1\,r121}
$$

Therefore, **BMI = 31** (to the nearest whole number), which places it in the
same category (obese) as indicated on the Body Mass Index chart.

C

1 stone = 14 lbs

So, 11 stone and 6 pounds = (11 x 14) + 6 = 154 + 6 = 160 lbs
160 lbs crosses 5' 9" just within the Normal Range (18.5 – 25) of the
Body Mass Index.

g

The first number shows your distance from an eye chart in feet.
The second number refers to the size of letter you can read

h

$\frac{\textbf{120}}{\textbf{80}}$ mm Hg

The top number refers to Systolic Blood Pressure (the force exerted by the
blood on the walls of the arteries as the heart muscle contracts to pump
blood around the body).

The bottom number refers to Diastolic Blood Pressure (the force exerted
by the blood on the walls of the arteries as the heart muscle relaxes
between beats).

j

32 for an adult including: 8 incisors, 4 canines, 8 premolars and 12 molars
(which include the 4 wisdom teeth).

20 for young children below the age of six:

k

38 inches for a man and **35 inches** for a woman

l

30 minutes a day

m

635 litres per second

n

Decibels on a scale from 0 to 140

o

24,902 miles   40,075 km

p

238,857miles   384,403 km

q

25 million miles   40.5 million km

r

93 million miles   150 million km

s

330 metres per second (330m/s)

t

670,616,629 mph   299,792,458 m/s

Answers to L3 Numeracy Learning Guide

Q1a £337,104,120,000 in standard form = **3.3710412 x 10¹¹**

Q1b Value of painting = £23,500,000

The value of the painting as a percentage of the country's assets =

$$\frac{23,500,000}{337,104,120,000} \times 100\% = \frac{235,000}{33,710,412} \% = \mathbf{6.9711 \times 10^{-3}}$$

Q2 Diameter of one atom = 10^{-8} cm = 10^{-10}m
150,000 atoms = 1.5×10^5
So, length of atoms = $1.5 \times 10^5 \times 10^{-10}$m = $1.5 \times \mathbf{10^{-5}}$m

Q3a To calculate distance CB,

Speed = 42 miles per hour Time = 42 minutes = $\frac{42}{60} = \frac{21}{30} = \frac{7}{10}$ = 0.7 hours

$$Speed = \frac{Distance}{Time}$$

and Distance (CB) = Speed x Time = 42 x 0.7 = 29.4 miles

AB can be calculated by using pythagorus theorem
$AC^2 = CB^2 + AB^2$
$(63)^2 = (29.4)^2 + (AB)^2$
$(AB)^2 = (63)^2 - (29.4)^2 = 3969 - 864.36 = 3,104.64$

Therefore, AB = $\sqrt{3,104.64}$ = 55.719 miles (to 3 decimal places)
0.621 miles = 1km

$1 \text{ mile} = \frac{1}{0.621} \text{ km} = 1.61\text{km}$

55.719 miles = 55.719 x 1.61km = 89.708km (to 3dp)
The car emits 0.27kg per kilometre = 89.708 x 0.27 = **24.221**kg (to 3dp)

Q3b   To calculate angle BAC:

$$\text{Sine (BAC)} = \frac{\text{Opposite}}{\text{Hypotenuse}} = \frac{BC}{AC} = \frac{29.4}{63} = 0.467 \text{ (to 3 dp)}$$

Therefore, angle BAC = **27.8°** (to 1 dp)

$$\text{Cosine (BAC)} = \frac{\text{Adjacent}}{\text{Hypotenuse}} = \frac{AB}{AC} = \frac{55.719}{63} = 0.884 \text{ (to 3 dp)}$$

Therefore, angle BAC = **27.8°** (to 1 dp)

Q4a   Area of field = 1.8 Hectares = 1.8 x 10,000m² = 18,000m²
So, area of field = length of field x width of field = 18,000m²
Length of field = 2 x width of field
If we say the width of the field is Y, then the length of the field is 2Y

Area of field then = 2Y x Y = 2Y²

2Y² = 18,000m² $Y^2 = \dfrac{18,000}{2} = 9,000m^2$

Y² = 9,000m² Y = √9,000 = 30m

Therefore, length of field = 2 x 30m = **60m** and width of field = **30m**

Q4b   Scale = 1: 200
On the scale drawing, length of field = 60m ÷ 200 = 6,000cm ÷ 200
6,0~~00~~cm ÷ 2~~00~~ = 60 ÷ 2 = 30cm

Therefore, on scale drawing, length of field
= **30**cm and width of field = **15**cm

Q5a   Let the number of flights to France sold = A and
the number of flights to Germany sold = B

Then, **A + B = 380** (Equation 1)

and, **£33.50A + £37.00B = £13,629.50** (Equation 2)

Q5b   If A + B = 380 then A = 380 – B
We can now substitute A = 380 – B into equation 2:
So, 33.50(380 – B) + 37B = 13,629.50

Next, we expand the brackets:

33.50 x 380 – 33.5B + 37B = 13,629.50

12,730 +3.5B = 13,629.50

Therefore, 3.5B = 13,629.50 – 12,730 = 899.5

3.5B = 8,995 B = $\dfrac{899.5}{3.5}$ = **257** = number of flights to Germany sold

We can now substitute B = 257 into equation 1

A + 257 = 380 so A = 380 – 257

= **123** = number of flights to France sold

The Numeracy Challenge (Answers)

Q1 If a man earns £6.75 per hour, then calculate how much he would earn in a 37 hour week.

£6.75 x 37

(37 = 30 + 7)

£6.75 x 30 = £67.50   £6.75 x 7 = £6.75
              x   3   x   7
            £ 202.50   £ 47.25
               2 1   5 3

So, £6.48 x 37   =   202.50
              +   47.25
            £ **249.75**

Q2 Calculate 13.5% of £250.00

10% = £25.00   1% = £2.50   0.5% = £1.25

                        3% = 2.50
                           x   3
                         £ 7.50
                            1

13.5% = 10% + 3% + 0.5% =   25.00
                             7.50
                             1.25
                       £ **33.75**
                         1

Q3 Calculate the volume of concrete used in the construction of an industrial warehouse floor, which has the following dimensions:

Length = 25m Width = 12m Depth = 300mm

Depth = 300mm = 30cm = $\dfrac{3\,m}{10}$ (= 0.3m)

Volume = Length x Width x Depth

$$= 12 \times \cancel{25}^{5} \times \frac{3}{\cancel{10}^{2}} = \frac{180}{2} = \textbf{90m}^3 \text{ of concrete}$$

Alternatively (although a bit more long winded):

$25 \times 0.3 = (20 + 5) \times 0.3 = (20 \times 0.3) + (5 \times 0.3) = 6 + 1.5 = 7.5$

Then, $12 \times 7\_ = (12 \times 7) + (12 \times \_) = 84 + 6 = \textbf{90m}^3$ of concrete

Q4 If the cost of 1.5kg bag of rice is £2.40 then calculate the cost of 400g of that rice.

1.5kg = 1,500g

If the cost of 1,500g is £2.40 then the cost per gram is $\dfrac{£2.40}{1,500}$

and the cost of 400g is $\dfrac{£2.40 \times \cancel{400}}{\cancel{1,500}} = \dfrac{£2.40 \times 4}{15} = \dfrac{£9.60}{15} = \dfrac{96}{150}$

Top and bottom are divisible by 3, so $\dfrac{96}{150} = \dfrac{32}{50} = \dfrac{64}{100} = 0.64 = \textbf{£0.64}$

Q5 If the exchange rate between the Euro and the pound is: **1 Euro** = **£0.91** then calculate how many Euros (to the nearest cent) you would get from **£70.00**

1 Euro = £0.91   or   £0.91 = 1 Euro

If we divide both sides by 0.91, then $\dfrac{£0.91}{0.91} = \dfrac{1}{0.91}$ Euro

So, $£1 = \dfrac{1}{0.91}$ Euro

Then, if we multiply both sides by 70, $70 \times £1 = 70 \times \dfrac{1}{0.91}$ Euro

So, $£70 = \dfrac{70}{0.91}$ Euro

This, naturally, would not be easy to solve since it would involve carrying out the following tricky division:

$0.91 \overline{\smash{)}\,70.00}$

However, to get rid of the decimal point in the 0.91 we can multiply the top and bottom by 100 i.e. $\dfrac{70}{0.91} = \dfrac{70 \times 100}{0.91 \times 100} = \dfrac{7{,}000}{91}$

This, however, would still involve dividing 7,000 by 91 which is not too easy either. To make it a little simpler, we could factorise it since 7 will go into 91 13 times.

So, $\dfrac{^1 7{,}000}{9\!\!\!/ 1^{13}} = \dfrac{1{,}000}{13}$

This at least then is a little easier to solve:

$\dfrac{76.923}{13\,\overline{)100^9 0.^{12}0^3 0^4 0^1 0}} =$ **76.92** Euros (to the nearest cent)

When explaining this problem to students, we can put across the idea that with any equation we can do the same to both sides of that equation or the same to the top (nominator) and bottom (denominator) of either side of an equation, and still keep it balanced.

In this particular problem, we are dividing both sides of the equation by 0.91 (in order to find an expression for how many Euros there are in £1), then multiplying both sides of the equation by 70 (in order to find an expression for how many Euros there are in £70), then multiplying the top and bottom of the equation by 100 (in order to remove the decimal point from the denominator) and then dividing the top and bottom by 7 (in order to simplify the equation).

To help clarify and reinforce the above methods, we can compare them with something more familiar, for example:

$8 \times 3 = 24$ and $\dfrac{8 \times 3}{4} = \dfrac{24}{4} = 6$

$4 \times 2 = 8$ and $4 \times 2 \times 100 = 8 \times 100 = 800$

The above methods can also be used in the context of introducing algebra, and/or manipulating and simplifying equations, for example:

$2.5a = b \quad \dfrac{2.5a}{2.5} = \dfrac{b}{2.5} \quad a = \dfrac{b}{2.5} = \dfrac{b \times 10}{2.5 \times 10} = \dfrac{b \times 10}{25} = \dfrac{10b}{25} = \dfrac{2b}{5} = 0.4b$

Alternatively:

$2.5a = b \quad 10 \times 2.5a = 10 \times b \quad 25a = 10b \quad a = \dfrac{10b}{25} = 0.4b$

Q6 The thickness of the ten pence piece is being increased in January 2011 from 1.7mm to 1.9mm. Calculate the percentage increase in the thickness of the coin (to the nearest whole number).

Percentage increase = $\dfrac{\text{actual increase}}{\text{original amount}}$ x 100%

actual increase = 1.9mm – 1.7mm = 0.2mm   original amount = 1.7mm

So, % increase = $\dfrac{0.2}{1.7}$ x 100% = $\dfrac{20}{1.7}$ = $\dfrac{200}{17}$ = $17\overline{)20^30.^{13}0}$ $\dfrac{1\,1.\,7}{}$ (r 11)

= 12% (to the nearest whole number)